Chemistry
Laboratory Manual
Fourth Edition

Nancy De Luca

Department of Chemistry
University of Massachusetts Lowell

Fall 2012

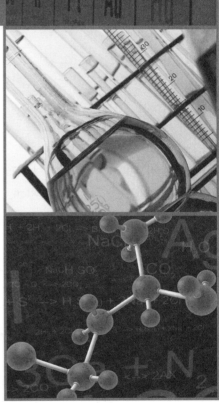

HAYDEN
HM
McNEIL

Hayden-McNeil Publishing
14903 Pilot Drive
Plymouth, MI 48170
www.hmpublishing.com

DeLuca 5517-6 F12

Table of Contents

Appendices

Laboratory Safety Rules

Certain practices and procedures must be followed to avoid accidents in the chemistry laboratory. Read over the rules and consult with the teaching staff if you have any questions. After you have read and understand the rules, sign the form which follows and turn it in to your laboratory instructor. Failure to obey the rules can result in dismissal from the course.

1. Responsible behavior is required at all times.

2. University-approved safety glasses are required **at all times**. Consult the special instructions on the purchase of safety glasses. Contact lenses are **never permitted** to be worn in the laboratory as vapors can collect under the lenses.

3. Only authorized experiments are permitted in the presence of a teaching assistant or instructor.

4. No smoking, eating, or drinking is permitted in the laboratory.

5. No sandals or open-toed shoes are permitted in the laboratory. If you wear sandals, you will be sent home to change your shoes.

6. Proper clothing (coverage from the shoulders to the knees) must be worn in the laboratory. If you are not properly dressed, you will be sent home to change.

7. If an accident occurs, no matter how minor, report it to your laboratory instructor.

8. During the presentation on laboratory safety, learn the locations and operation of the hoods, eyewash, fire extinguishers, fire blankets and showers.

9. Keep the benchtops and hood tops clear of your belongings. Only a pen, Kimwipes and the lab manual should be on the benchtop along with the needed lab equipment. Chairs are to be put away after the instructor has presented the material for the experiment to be performed.

10. To avoid accidents, check all glassware before using it and discard items which are chipped or cracked. Check with your instructor before discarding any special glassware. If an object has been heated, check carefully for radiant heat **before** touching it. Read all labels carefully to make sure you have the correct chemical.

11. Dispose of all chemical waste as directed by your instructor or the laboratory manual.

12. It is your responsibility to clean **all** the equipment used for a given experiment. This includes the items in your locker as well as special equipment distributed by the instructor. If you spill any chemicals or drop glassware, check with your instructor as to how to clean it up. No solid items should be put down the sink, and you and your classmates should check the drains before leaving the lab. Make sure you wipe off your benchtop and wash your hands before leaving the laboratory.

Safety Agreement

I have attended the safety lecture given by my laboratory instructor and have read the *Safety Rules* in this manual. Whenever I am in the laboratory, I will use good safety practices and behave in an orderly and professional manner. I am agreeing that while in the chemistry laboratory I will follow these safety precautions:

1. I will wear approved safety glasses at all times. I will not wear contact lenses.

2. I know the exact locations of the hoods, eyewash, fire extinguishers, fire blankets, first aid kits and showers, and I know how and when to use them.

3. I will not work in any laboratory when the instructor is not present, nor will I perform unauthorized experiments or procedures.

4. I will not eat, drink, or smoke in the laboratory or use laboratory containers for food or drink, nor will I taste, touch, or directly smell any chemical. If I need to leave the lab, I will shut down my experiment, wash my hands, and notify my instructor.

5. I will store everything except my pen, Kimwipes, and lab manual away from the lab benches, and put my chair away at the end of the lab lecture.

6. I will wear proper clothing in the lab.

7. I will avoid touching hot objects and using broken glassware, and I will check the label on each dispensing container twice before using it.

8. I will dispose of chemicals used in each experiment as directed.

9. I will immediately notify my instructor of any accident or injury which occurs, no matter how minor. I will seek additional first aid at the Health Center or hospital, if the instructor or staff supervisor directs me to do so, and I will see to it that the instructor or staff supervisor is notified as soon as possible of the outcome.

10. I will quickly clean up any breakage or spills, and will consult with my instructor for the correct method of cleanup and disposal.

11. At the end of the laboratory period, I will clean up the equipment I have used, wash my work area, help clean up the common areas and wash my hands. I will then have my instructor lock my equipment drawer and sign my data sheet.

Signature		Date	Course	Section #	Room

Locker #	Laboratory Instructor

Safety Agreement

I have attended the safety lecture given by my laboratory instructor and have read the *Safety Rules* in this manual. Whenever I am in the laboratory, I will use good safety practices and behave in an orderly and professional manner. I am agreeing that while in the chemistry laboratory I will follow these safety precautions:

1. I will wear approved safety glasses at all times. I will not wear contact lenses.

2. I know the exact locations of the hoods, eyewash, fire extinguishers, fire blankets, first aid kits and showers, and I know how and when to use them.

3. I will not work in any laboratory when the instructor is not present, nor will I perform unauthorized experiments or procedures.

4. I will not eat, drink, or smoke in the laboratory or use laboratory containers for food or drink, nor will I taste, touch, or directly smell any chemical. If I need to leave the lab, I will shut down my experiment, wash my hands, and notify my instructor.

5. I will store everything except my pen, Kimwipes, and lab manual away from the lab benches, and put my chair away at the end of the lab lecture.

6. I will wear proper clothing in the lab.

7. I will avoid touching hot objects and using broken glassware, and I will check the label on each dispensing container twice before using it.

8. I will dispose of chemicals used in each experiment as directed.

9. I will immediately notify my instructor of any accident or injury which occurs, no matter how minor. I will seek additional first aid at the Health Center or hospital, if the instructor or staff supervisor directs me to do so, and I will see to it that the instructor or staff supervisor is notified as soon as possible of the outcome.

10. I will quickly clean up any breakage or spills, and will consult with my instructor for the correct method of cleanup and disposal.

11. At the end of the laboratory period, I will clean up the equipment I have used, wash my work area, help clean up the common areas and wash my hands. I will then have my instructor lock my equipment drawer and sign my data sheet.

Signature	Date	Course	Section #	Room

Locker #	Laboratory Instructor

x

1 Experiment

Weighing

I. Introduction

During the semester you will become familiar with several different devices which can be used to determine the mass of an object. In the beginning you will use the less precise scales, the decigram (sensitive to .1 gram) and centigram (sensitive to .01 gram) balances. These balances work much in the same way that a doctor's scale operates. Weights are pushed along metal beams until the pointer falls. The last weight added is pushed back a notch, and then weights are slid along the next beam until a balance is reached. The combined readings of the weights on all the beams is the mass of the object being weighed. Balances of this type vary somewhat, but the principle of operation remains the same.

For more precise measurement of mass, an analytical or substitution balance is used. These instruments are extremely delicate and sensitive, measuring to within .0001 grams. There are two types of substitution balances in the laboratory, mechanical ones and electronic ones. Both are extremely delicate and quite expensive, so handle them gently.

II. Equipment Needed

This experiment requires the following:

- 3 – 100 mL beakers (labeled)
- 3 – 250 mL beakers (labeled)
- 2 weighing unknowns (from instructor)

III. Procedure

A. General Operation of Beam Balances

1. Make sure all weights on the beams are in the zero position. With nothing on the pan the pointer should line up with the zero. If it does not line up, ask your instructor to zero the scale. Do not attempt to zero the balance on your own. In this course all measurements will be made by difference. That is, the object to be weighed will be weighed in a container, then the empty container will be weighed. In this method, if a scale is not at zero, the error will be eliminated when the mass of the empty container is subtracted from the mass of the object plus the container. For this reason it is crucial that you **use the same balance for all measurements.**

2. The decigram balance is a triple beam balance. The middle beam has a capacity of 500 grams, with each notch equaling 100 grams. The back beam has a capacity of 100 grams, with each notch equaling 10 grams. The front beam has a slide, and a total capacity of 10 grams. The scale is marked off in tenths of a gram.

3. Starting with the largest capacity beam (500 g), move the weight to the right to the first notch which causes the pointer to drop, then move it back one notch causing the pointer to rise.

4. Repeat step three with the 100 gram weight.

5. Slide the 10 g weight to the position which brings the pointer to rest at zero. The weight of the object is the sum of all the positions, read directly from the beams. If the slider is exactly on a line, the hundredths place should be noted as a zero. If slightly above or below a line, **estimate the hundredths place** as shown below.

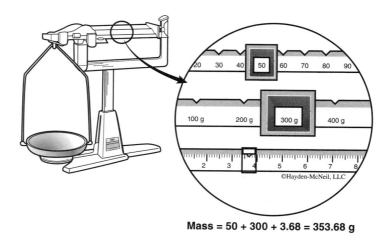

Mass = 50 + 300 + 3.68 = 353.68 g

Figure 1-1. Triple beam balance.

6. The operation of the centigram balance is similar. Start with the rear (200 g) beam, moving the weight to the right until the pointer drops, and then go back a notch. Repeat with the 100 g weight, and then the 10 gram weight. The front

beam has a slider which represents a total mass of 1 gram. It is graduated in hundredths of a gram. **Estimate one place beyond the hundredths place** to indicate if the slide is directly on, above, or below a line on the slider scale.

B. Specific Instructions for the Decigram Weighing Experiment

1. Obtain two unknowns from your laboratory instructor. One unknown will be weighed on the decigram balance, the other will be weighed on the centigram balance. Record both unknown code numbers on your data sheet in ink.

2. Clean and dry three 100 mL beakers. Label them for present and future use. Bring your beakers and your decigram unknown to a decigram balance. The unknown consists of the tube, cap, and the contents. **Do not open the unknown tube.**

3. Following the procedure outlined previously, weigh beaker #1. Record the mass of the empty beaker to the nearest hundredth of a gram on the data sheet. Remove the beaker from the balance.

4. Place the entire unknown tube (including cap) in beaker #1, gently return it to the balance pan, weigh it, and record your data.

5. Repeat steps 3 and 4 using beaker #2 and beaker #3 and the same unknown.

C. Specific Instructions for the Centigram Weighing Experiment

1. Make sure you have recorded your unknown code numbers on the data sheet.

2. Clean and dry three 250 mL beakers, and label them #1, #2, and #3.

3. Following the general weighing procedures above, weigh beaker #1 on the centigram balance and record the mass (to the nearest thousandth of a gram), in ink, on the data sheet. Remove the beaker from the balance pan.

4. Gently place the entire unknown (tube, cap, and contents) in the beaker and reweigh. Record your data.

5. Repeat steps 3 and 5 using beaker #2 and beaker #3. Record your data.

6. Before leaving the laboratory, return both unknowns to your instructor and have your instructor sign your data sheet and lock your equipment drawer.

IV. Calculations

In this experiment, all weights are obtained three times, using different beakers as the weighing container. On the laboratory report you will be asked to calculate the average mass of each unknown, along with the deviation, the average deviation, and the percent deviation.

The deviation is calculated for each trial as follows:

$$\text{deviation} = \text{trial result} - \text{average value}$$

4

The average deviation is:

$$\frac{\text{the sum of the absolute values of the deviation}}{\text{\# of trials}}$$

The percent deviation is:

$$\frac{\text{average deviation}}{\text{average value}} \times 100\%$$

[Report Form]

Name	Section #

Instructor's Signature	Date

Weighing—Data, Calculations, and Results

I. Data
Record data in ink (include units).

A. Decigram Balance: Unknown # _____

	Test 1	Test 2	Test 3
a. Weight of beaker + unknown	_____	_____	_____
b. Weight of empty beaker	_____	_____	_____

B. Centigram Balance: Unknown # _____

	Test 1	Test 2	Test 3
a. Weight of beaker + unknown	_____	_____	_____
b. Weight of empty beaker	_____	_____	_____

II. Calculations
A. Decigram Balance:

a. Weight of unknown   _____   _____   _____

b. Mean weight of unknown—show calculation

_____

c. Deviation—show calculations

_____   _____   _____

6

    d.   Average deviation—show calculation

                                    _____

    e.   Percent deviation—show calculation

                                      _____

B. Centigram Balance

    a.   Weight of unknown   _____   _____   _____

    b.   Mean weight of unknown—show calculation

                                        _____

    c.   Deviation—show calculation

                                      _____   _____   _____

    d.   Average deviation—show calculation

                                        _____

    e.   Percent deviation—show calculation

                                        _____

III. Results

A. Decigram Balance:

Unknown # _____ has an average mass of _____ ± _____ g
(average deviation)

B. Centigram Balance:

Unknown # _____ has an average mass of _____ ± _____ g
(average deviation)

2 Experiment

Volume of Liquids

I. Introduction

There are several pieces of equipment that are used in the laboratory to measure the volume of liquids. Each has a different purpose and level of accuracy. Graduated cylinders are used to measure variable volumes when there isn't a need for great accuracy. Burets are used to deliver variable volumes of liquids with considerably greater accuracy than a graduated cylinder. Volumetric pipets are precisely made to deliver a specific volume if properly used. Volumetric flasks are precisely made to contain a single specified volume, and are used to make solutions with accurately known concentration.

In this experiment, you will use several of these devices to measure the volume of samples of water. You will determine the accuracy of each device by weighing the water and using the density to calculate the volume of water actually delivered.

A. Graduated Cylinders

Graduated cylinders are used to measure amounts of liquids when the volume can be approximate. The cylinders come in various sizes, and although larger cylinders exist, they are routinely used to measure volumes of 100 mL or less. When using a graduated cylinder, the surface of the liquid may be curved. This curvature of the liquid surface is called a *meniscus*, and it results from attraction of the liquid and the material of the cylinder. To take an accurate reading, the center of the meniscus must be at eye level.

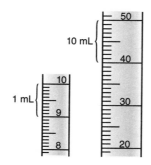

**Comparison of the graduations on a
10 mL and a 100 mL graduated cylinder**

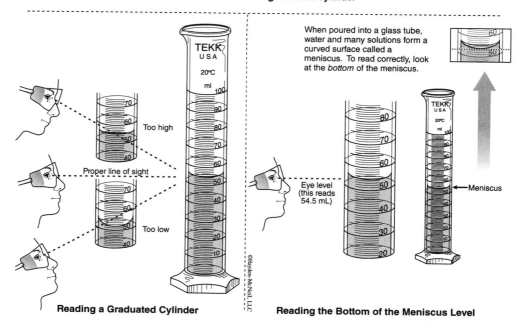

Reading a Graduated Cylinder   **Reading the Bottom of the Meniscus Level**

When poured into a glass tube, water and many solutions form a curved surface called a meniscus. To read correctly, look at the *bottom* of the meniscus.

Note that the volume contained in the cylinder is read from the bottom up, and that the reading should be estimated one place beyond the divisions on the cylinder. If the cylinder is marked in tenths of a mL, estimate to the hundredth of a mL.

B. Pipets

Pipets provide a more precise measurement of volume than graduated cylinders. They are often used if you need to measure out the same volume of a liquid several times. There are two different kinds of pipets, and both come in several different sizes. The Mohr pipet is calibrated, with various volumes marked on it, so it can deliver a variety of volumes.

Graduations stop at base mark

Mohr (drain-out)

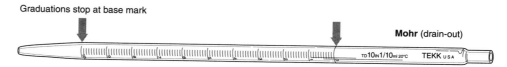

The volumetric pipet is designed to deliver only a particular volume. It is very precisely made, and when properly used, delivers very precise volumes. It will have a single line on it, along with its capacity stamped on the barrel of the pipet.

Pipets are filled using a rubber bulb to create suction so that the liquid can be drawn up into the pipet. **Never pipet by mouth**. In this experiment, you will be using a simple rubber bulb equipped with a plastic tip. The procedure for using a pipet is illustrated below.

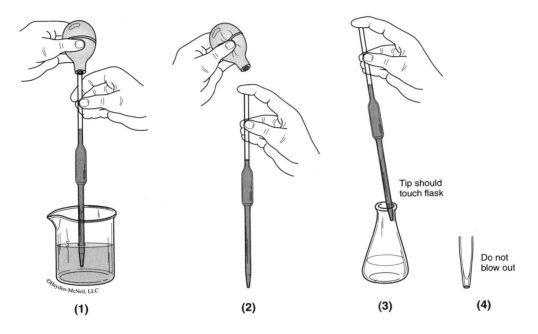

Tip should
touch flask

Do not
blow out

©Hayden-McNeil, LLC

(1)   (2)   (3)   (4)

With the tip of the pipet in a beaker containing the liquid to be transferred, squeeze the rubber bulb and then *gently* press the plastic tip against the opening at the top of the pipet to provide suction. **Do not place the barrel of the pipet into the rubber bulb or plastic tip**. Keep the tip of the pipet below the liquid surface in the beaker, and provide enough suction to draw the liquid 1–2 inches above the calibration line on the pipet. Quickly remove the bulb, and place your index finger on the opening on the top of the pipet to keep the liquid from flowing out. Gently release the pressure of your index finger and allow the liquid level to fall slowly until it reaches the calibration mark on the pipet. Keeping the pipet vertical, insert the tip into the flask or beaker that is to receive the sample, and let the liquid drain out of the pipet. Touch the tip of the pipet to the inside wall of the flask. A small amount of liquid will remain in the tip of the pipet. **Do not blow out the last bit of liquid from the pipet**. The pipet is designed to have a small amount of liquid remaining, and has been calibrated accordingly.

Pipets must be properly cleaned before use. They should first be washed with soap and water, rinsed with tap water, and then rinsed with small portions of distilled water. To test if the pipet is clean enough, water should not bead up anywhere within the inside of the pipet. To keep the rinse water from diluting a liquid that is to be measured with the pipet, the pipet is rinsed with several small portions of the liquid to be measured, and the rinsings discarded into a waste beaker.

If you are measuring several liquids with the same pipet, rinse with distilled water between liquids, and then rinse with several small portions of the next liquid to be measured. After use, rinse the pipet with distilled water so that no chemicals remain in the pipet.

C. Burets

Burets are used when various sample sizes of liquids must be dispensed or measured precisely. The buret is a long calibrated tube (usually 50 mL) with a valve at the bottom called a stopcock.

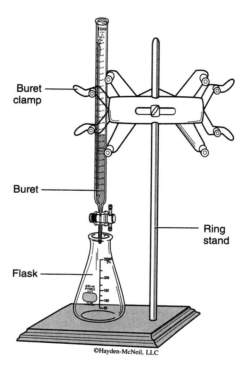

Buret clamp

Buret

Ring stand

Flask

©Hayden-McNeil, LLC

When using a buret, an initial and a final reading of volume are made. The difference between the two values is the volume of liquid delivered by the buret. It is important to note that volume is read down from the top of the buret, and not up from the bottom. As with a graduated cylinder, you should be at eye level with the meniscus, and estimate one place beyond the divisions on the buret. The buret illustrated below has a reading of 18.77 or 18.78 mL. The last digit is assumed to be an estimate.

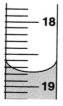

18

19

When using a buret, you do not need to and shouldn't try to start exactly at the 0.00 mL mark. You simply need an accurate beginning and end volume. It's also much easier to start with a liquid level that is at the proper height for you to read easily, at your eye level. When filling a buret, always use a small funnel, and position the top of the buret at eye level, so you're not pouring over your head. Once filled, remove the funnel so that no more liquid drips into the buret. You must also run the liquid through the tip of the buret to remove any air bubbles before you take your initial reading.

Burets are first cleaned with soap and water using a bristle brush with a long handle. The buret is then rinsed with tap water, followed by several rinsings with distilled water. Prior to use, the buret is rinsed with several small portions of the liquid to be measured, and the rinsings are collected in a waste beaker. After use, the buret should be rinsed with distilled water to remove any chemicals remaining.

II. Equipment Needed

This experiment requires the following:

- 50 mL graduated cylinder
- 10 mL graduated cylinder
- pipet and pipet bulb (from instructor)
- buret and clamp (from instructor)
- small funnel
- watch glass
- 50 mL plastic beaker (from instructor)
- thermometer (from instructor)

III. Procedure

A. The Graduated Cylinder

1. Clean and dry your **50 mL graduated cylinder,** 50 mL beaker, and a watch glass to cover the beaker.

2. Weigh the beaker with watch glass on the Cent-O-Gram balance and record the mass (to the nearest 0.001 g) on the data sheet.

3. Obtain approximately 100 mL of distilled water in a clean Erlenmeyer flask. Measure and record the temperature of the water on the data sheet.

4. Fill the graduated cylinder to the 10 mL mark with distilled water. Transfer the contents of the graduated cylinder to the dry weighed 50 mL beaker.

5. Cover the beaker with the watch glass and weigh the beaker, watch glass, and water on the Cent-O-Gram balance and record the mass (to the nearest 0.001 g) on the data sheet.

6. Estimate the volume of the water using the markings on the 50 mL beaker and record your estimate.

7. Empty and dry the beaker.

8. Clean and dry your **10 mL graduated cylinder** and repeat steps 4, 5, and 6.

9. Empty the beaker and dry it for Part B of the experiment.

B. The Pipet

1. Obtain a pipet and a rubber safety bulb from your instructor.

2. Clean the pipet with soap and water, rinse the pipet with tap water, and then with small portions of distilled water.

3. Practice filling the pipet and dispensing distilled water from the pipet, following the method outlined in the introduction section of this experiment. Consult with your instructor if you experience difficulty in using the pipet.

4. Obtain approximately 100 mL of distilled water in a clean Erlenmeyer flask. Measure and record the temperature of the water on the data sheet.

5. Fill the pipet to the line with distilled water and carefully transfer the water sample to your dry weighed 50 mL beaker.

6. Cover the beaker with the watch glass and weigh the beaker, watch glass, and water sample on the Cent-O-Gram balance and record the mass (to the nearest 0.001 g) on the data sheet.

7. Estimate the volume of the water using the markings on the 50 mL beaker and record your estimate.

8. Before proceeding, use the mass of water delivered and its density to calculate its volume. See the section on calculations. Compare the actual volume, based on mass, and the volume of the pipet. If the first three significant figures of the volumes are not the same, you should practice using the pipet and repeat this section of the experiment.

9. Return the pipet and bulb to the instructor.

C. The Buret

1. Obtain a buret, clamp, and ring stand and set up the apparatus on your lab bench.

2. Using a funnel and a beaker, fill the buret with tap water, and make sure that there are no leaks from the stopcock. If the stopcock leaks, have your instructor try to adjust it and make sure that all the washers are present. If the buret still leaks, obtain another one.

3. Clean the buret as described in the introduction part of this experiment. Clean it with soap and water and a buret brush, then rinse it with tap water and then small portions of distilled water. Make sure that the soap, tap water, and distilled water also go through the stopcock and rinse the inside of the buret tip.

4. Lower the top of the buret so it is at or below eye level, and using a funnel, fill the buret above the zero line with distilled water. Allow some of the water to run out through the tip into a beaker or flask. The water should flow down in sheets along the inside of the buret. If droplets form, the buret should be cleaned again using the brush and soap and water. Repeat steps 3 and 4 until clean.

5. Lower the top of the buret so it is at or below eye level, and using a small funnel, refill the buret with distilled water to a volume somewhat below the zero mark. Remove the funnel. Run some water through the tip to make sure there are no air bubbles.

6. With the meniscus at eye level, estimate the initial buret reading to the nearest 0.02 mL. Record the reading on the data sheet.

7. Clean and dry a 150 mL beaker and watch glass and weigh them on the Cent-O-Gram balance and record the mass (to the nearest 0.001 g) on the data sheet.

8. Place the dry weighed 150 mL beaker under the buret, and lower the buret so that the tip is below the edge of the beaker. Open the stopcock of the buret and allow approximately 25 mL of water to flow into the beaker. Close the stopcock and record the volume reading on the buret.

9. Weigh the beaker, watch glass, and water on the Cent-O-Gram balance to the nearest 0.001 g. Record the mass of water on the data sheet.

10. Measure the temperature of the water and record it on the data sheet.

11. Before proceeding, use the mass of water delivered and its density to calculate its volume. See the section on calculations. Compare the actual volume, based on mass, and the volume from the buret readings. If the first three significant figures of the volumes are not the same, you should practice using the buret and repeat this section of the experiment.

12. Return the buret to the instructor.

13. Have your instructor sign your report form and lock your drawer before leaving the laboratory.

IV. Calculations

In each section of the experiment, the volume of water, as measured using different types of glassware, will be compared to the actual volume of water that is calculated using mass and density. Density is the mass of a substance divided by its volume.

$$\text{density} = \delta = \frac{\text{mass}}{\text{volume}}$$

For liquids, density is usually expressed in g/mL. The density of liquids varies with temperature. The appendix contains the density of water at various temperatures. You will use the density of water (for the temperature of water used) to calculate the volume of each water sample.

$$\text{volume} = \frac{\text{mass}}{\delta}$$

Be sure to pay attention to significant figures when calculating volumes.

14

[Report Form]

_____	
Name	Section #
_____	
Instructor's Signature	Date

Volume of Liquids—Data, Calculations, and Results

I. Data and Results
Record data in ink (include units).

A. The 50 mL Graduated Cylinder—Data

Mass of empty 50 mL beaker and watch glass   _____

Temperature of water   _____

Mass of 50 mL beaker, watch glass, and water   _____

Volume reading on 50 mL beaker   _____

Results:

Mass of water in 50 mL beaker   _____

Density of water   _____

Calculated volume of water (show calculation)

_____

Difference between graduated cylinder reading
and actual (calculated) volume

_____

Difference between beaker reading and
actual (calculated) volume

_____

The 10 mL Graduated Cylinder—Data

Mass of empty 50 mL beaker and watch glass
(from Part A on previous page)   _____

Temperature of water (from Part A)   _____

Mass of 50 mL beaker, watch glass, and water   _____

Volume reading on 50 mL beaker   _____

Results:

Mass of water in 50 mL beaker   _____

Density of water   _____

Calculated volume of water (show calculation)

                                                                 _____

Difference between graduated cylinder reading and
actual (calculated) volume

                                                                 _____

Difference between beaker reading and
actual (calculated) volume

                                                                 _____

B. The Pipet—Data

Mass of empty 50 mL beaker and
watch glass (from Part A)   _____

Temperature of water

	Trial 1	Trial 2 (if needed)
Volume of pipet (marked on barrel)	_____	_____

	Trial 1	Trial 2 (if needed)
Mass of 50 mL beaker, watch glass, and water	_____	_____

Results:

Mass of water in 50 mL beaker	_____	_____
Density of water		
	_____	_____
	Trial 1	Trial 2 (if needed)

[Report Form continued]

Name _____ Section # _____

Calculated volume of water (show calculation Trial 1)

_____	_____
Trial 1	**Trial 2 (if needed)**

Difference between pipet volume (marked on the pipet) and the calculated volume of water

_____	_____
Trial 1	**Trial 2 (if needed)**

	Trial 1	**Trial 2 (if needed)**
C. The Buret—Data		
Initial buret reading	_____	_____
Final buret reading	_____	_____
Mass of empty 150 mL beaker and watch glass	_____	_____
Temperature of water	_____	_____
Mass of 150 mL beaker, watch glass, and water	_____	_____

Results:

	Trial 1	**Trial 2 (if needed)**
Volume of water delivered by buret	_____	_____
Mass of water in 150 mL beaker	_____	_____
Density of water	_____	_____

Calculated volume of water (show calculation Trial 1)

_____	_____
Trial 1	**Trial 2 (if needed)**

18   Difference between buret volume and actual volume

———————————   ———————————

Trial 1   **Trial 2 (if needed)**

II. Conclusions

1. Based on your results, rank the accuracy of the beaker, graduated cylinder, pipet, and buret in measuring volume.

———————————————————————————————————————

least accurate → most accurate

2. Is the 10 mL or 50 mL graduated cylinder more accurate in measuring 10 mL of liquid? Support your answer by using your results from Part A.

III. Questions

1. A student filled his buret and took an initial reading. He accidentally left the funnel in the top of the buret, and a drop of water went into the buret after his initial reading. He then used the buret to deliver 13.48 mL of water, based on his initial and final readings. A drop of water is 0.05 mL.

    a. What volume of water was actually delivered by the buret?

    b. Calculate the % error as a result of the extra drop of water in the buret.

$$\% \text{ error} = \frac{|\text{ experimental value} - \text{actual value }|}{\text{actual value}}(100\%)$$

Answer: % error = ———————————

[Report Form continued]

_____
Name   Section #

2. A student forgot to run water through her buret, so there was an air bubble in the tip. She took her initial reading, and then delivered 17.80 mL of water based on her initial and final readings. The air bubble had a volume of 0.25 mL.

   a. What volume of water was actually delivered by the buret?

   b. Calculate the % error as a result of the air bubble in the buret.

   $$\% \text{ error} = \frac{|\text{ experimental value} - \text{actual value }|}{\text{actual value}}(100\%)$$

   Answer: % error = _____

3. Suppose your 25 mL pipet wasn't totally clean. When you tried to deliver the entire contents, three droplets of water remained on the inner walls of the pipet. Each droplet has a volume of 0.03 mL.

   a. What volume of water was actually delivered by the pipet?

   b. Calculate the % error as a result of the droplets of water in the pipet.

   $$\% \text{ error} = \frac{|\text{ experimental value} - \text{actual value }|}{\text{actual value}}(100\%)$$

   Answer: % error = _____

20

4. Suppose you need to make approximately 50 mL of a solution that is 15% by volume ethanol (a liquid organic alcohol) in water. Assuming the volumes are additive, and don't expand or contract when mixed,

   a. What volume of ethanol is needed? Show your calculation.

   b. What measuring device would you use to measure the ethanol? Explain your choice.

   c. What volume of water is needed? Show your calculation.

   d. What measuring device would you use to measure the water? Explain your choice.

5. You need to make 32.00 mL of a solution that contains benzene and toluene, two organic liquids. The solution needs to contain 25.00% by volume of toluene. Assume the volumes are additive, and don't expand or contract when mixed.

   a. What volume of toluene is needed? Show your calculation.

   b. What measuring device would you use to measure the toluene? Explain your choice.

   c. What volume of benzene is needed? Show your calculation.

   d. What measuring device would you use to measure the benzene? Explain your choice.

3 Experiment

Graphing

I. Introduction

Graphs are an extremely useful way of presenting experimental data. They present a visual representation of trends in data, and help scientists determine the mathematical relationship between the parameters that are graphed. In this activity, you will prepare several graphs, and use the graphs to determine the mathematical relationships between the quantities and parameters graphed. There are general instructions on graphing in the appendix of this manual.

Conventions in Graphing

The horizontal (x) axis of a graph is called the abscissa. The independent variable should be graphed on the x-axis. The independent variable is the property that the scientist is controlling. For example, if you are measuring the volume of a gas at various temperatures, temperature is the independent variable. Since changes in temperature will cause the gas to change volume, volume is the dependent variable. The dependent variable should be graphed on the vertical (y) axis. The y-axis is called the ordinate.

Graphs must be properly labeled with the parameter (volume, temperature, mass, etc.) and the units written in parenthesis. Graphs must also have a title written at the very top of the graph. An example might be, "Volume versus Temperature for Nitrogen Gas."

The graph must be properly scaled so that the data fills most of the graph. You do not want the data restricted to a small corner or area of the graph paper. You should select the scale and the lowest value for each axis based on the data you are graphing. You do not need to start at (x=0, y=0) in the lower left corner of the graph unless your data passes through or near the origin (0, 0). You should choose values for each line on the x-axis and each line on the y-axis so that your data fills most of the area of the graph. The scale you choose for the x-axis does not need to be the same as the scale for the y-axis. Clearly label values every 5 or 10 lines on each axis.

Data points should be clearly indicated by enclosing them within a circle, box, or triangle.

II. Materials

- several sheets of mm $\times$ mm grid graph paper

- a clear (see-through) ruler or straight edge

- a French curve or flexicurve ruler

- a pencil

- a calculator

III. Procedure and Report

In this activity, you will be provided with a variety of data to be graphed. You will make the graphs, analyze them, and perform calculations and answer questions about the graphs. You will hand in your completed report and graphs before leaving.

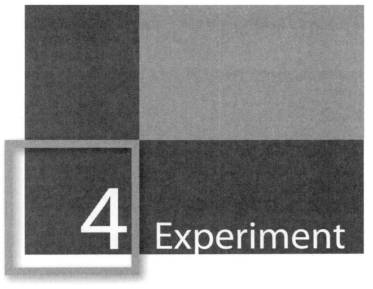

Density

I. Introduction

In this experiment you will determine the densities of solids and liquids using several different methods.

The density of a solid unknown will be determined using a graduated cylinder to determine the volume of the sample by the displacement method, and the decigram balance to determine the mass of the sample. Three trials will be performed.

The density of a liquid sample will be determined by two methods. In one, a graduated cylinder will be used to determine the volume of the sample, and the decigram balance will be used to determine the mass. Three trials will be performed.

The second method for liquid samples will use a device called a buret to measure the volume of liquid. A buret is much more accurate than a graduated cylinder for measuring volumes of liquids. You will also be using a more accurate balance to determine the mass of the sample. Instead of measuring the mass and volume of one sample and calculating the density, several mass and volume measurements will be performed, and the density determined graphically.

II. Equipment Needed

This experiment requires the following:

- solid and liquid density unknowns (from instructor)
- 1 small plastic beaker
- ring stand and clamp
- 50 mL graduated cylinder
- 2 – 100 mL plastic beakers

- 2-inch watch glass
- buret (from instructor)
- 1 funnel

III. Procedure

This procedure is divided into three sections. The sections can be performed in any order.

A. Determination of the Density of a Solid

1. Obtain a solid unknown (in a tube) from your laboratory instructor and record the code number on your laboratory report. Your unknown is the solid contained inside the plastic numbered tube.

2. Weigh a small plastic beaker using the decigram balance. The operation of the balance can be found in the *Weighing* experiment. Record the mass of the beaker, estimating to the nearest .01 of a gram, on the data sheet.

3. Place your solid unknown in the plastic beaker and reweigh. Record the mass of the beaker plus solid on the data sheet. The difference between the two weighings will be the mass of the solid unknown.

4. Place approximately 30 milliliters of tap water in a 50 mL graduated cylinder. Record the volume of water to the nearest tenth of a milliliter on the data sheet (see Figure 4-1).

5. Carefully place the solid unknown into the graduated cylinder without losing water by splashing. Tap the sides of the cylinder to dislodge any air bubbles and read and record the volume. The increase in volume will equal the volume of the solid object. Carefully pour out the contents of the cylinder into a beaker (not the sink), and remove and dry the solid unknown. Repeat steps 2–5 two more times with the same unknown. When finished, return the dry unknown, in its tube, to your instructor.

B. Determination of the Density of a Liquid Using a Graduated Cylinder

1. Clean and dry a 100 mL plastic beaker and a 2-inch watch glass which will be used to cover the beaker.

2. Obtain a liquid unknown sample from your instructor and record the code number on your data sheet. Transfer between 15 and 20 mL of your unknown to the 100 mL beaker and cover it with the watch glass. Be sure to leave the bottle containing the unknown tightly capped.

3. Weigh the beaker, contents, and watch glass on a decigram balance (see operating instructions in *Weighing* experiment). Estimate the mass to the nearest .01 of a gram, and record the value on the data sheet.

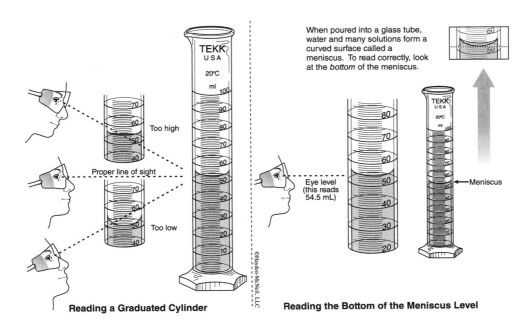

Figure 4-1. Reading the meniscus.

4. Transfer the liquid from the beaker to a clean and dry 50 mL graduated cylinder. Read the volume to the nearest 0.1 mL as described in Part A of this procedure.

5. Transfer the liquid unknown back to its original container and cap tightly.

6. Reweigh the beaker and watch glass and record the mass on the data sheet. The difference in the two weighings will be the weight of the liquid which was placed in the graduated cylinder.

7. Clean and dry the graduated cylinder and repeat steps 2–6 two more times using different volumes of the same liquid unknown. It is not necessary to clean and dry the beaker.

8. Clean all equipment when finished with the three determinations, and return the unknown liquid sample to your instructor.

C. Determination of Density of Water Using a Buret

1. Obtain a buret from your instructor. Thoroughly clean the buret with approximately 10 mL of soap solution and a buret brush. After rinsing the buret, including the tip, with several portions of tap water, "line the buret" with three 10 mL portions of distilled water. Your instructor will demonstrate this technique. Make sure that some of the distilled water is allowed to go through the tip of the buret.

2. Clamp the buret to the ring stand. Using a funnel, place approximately 45 mL of distilled water in the buret. Allow water to flow through the tip until there are no air bubbles present. Remove the funnel from the open end of the buret, and read and record the water level in the buret. Estimate to the nearest .01 mL and record the value on the data sheet. You do not need to start at the zero line, just record the initial water level. Read the bottom of the meniscus, being sure to read down from the top, rather than up from the bottom.

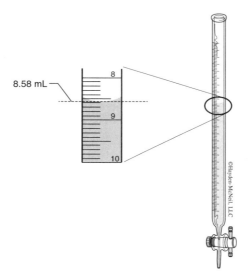

8.58 mL

3. Weigh a clean and dry 100 mL plastic beaker on the centigram balance (see operating instructions in *Weighing* experiment). Estimate the mass to the nearest 0.001 grams, and record the value on the data sheet. Be sure to use the same balance for all subsequent weighings.

4. Allow approximately 5–8 mL of water to flow from the buret into the beaker. Close the stopcock and record the water level in the buret on the data sheet. Estimate the reading to the nearest 0.01 mL.

5. Obtain the mass of the beaker and water using the same centigram balance. Estimate to the nearest 0.001 gram and record the mass on the data sheet.

6. Use the buret to add an additional sample of 5–8 mL of water to the beaker. Record the buret reading after addition, and reweigh the beaker containing the two portions of distilled water. Record all values on the data sheet.

7. Repeat step 6 three more times by adding three more portions of water and weighing the beaker plus water and obtaining the buret readings between additions. Record all buret readings and masses on the data sheet.

8. Obtain a thermometer from your laboratory instructor and determine the temperature of the water and record it (to the nearest 0.1°C) on the data sheet.

9. Dispose of all water in the sink, and fully drain the buret. Return all unknowns and special equipment to your instructor, and have your instructor sign your data sheet and lock your drawer before leaving the laboratory.

IV. Calculations

In this experiment you will determine the density of a solid as well as a liquid unknown and distilled water. Regardless of the nature of the sample, density is defined as the ratio of mass per unit volume. For most solids and liquids, the unit of mass is the gram, and the unit of volume can be either the milliliter or the cubic centimeter, as these units of volume are equivalent.

$$\text{density} = \frac{\text{mass (g)}}{\text{volume (mL or cm}^3\text{)}}$$

Thus, the common units of density are g/mL or g/cm^3. In determining the density of the solid (Part A), the mass of the solid (after subtracting the mass of the empty container) is divided by the volume of water displaced by the object to obtain the density. The average of three trials should be reported, with units, in the table of results. Pay close attention to significant figures. When more than one trial is performed, the results of individual trials can be compared to the average result. The **deviation** is the difference between the trial result and the average. The **average deviation** is the sum of the absolute values of the deviation divided by the number of trials. The **percent deviation** is the average deviation divided by the average value times 100%.

$$\text{deviation} = \text{value of trial} - \text{average value}$$

$$\text{average deviation} = \frac{\text{sum of abs. value of deviation}}{\text{\# of trials}}$$

$$\text{percent deviation} = \frac{\text{average deviation}}{\text{average value}} \times 100\%$$

The density of the liquid obtained using the graduated cylinder and decigram balance is also obtained directly by dividing the mass of each sample by the volume of each sample. Report the average of your three trials, the deviations, average deviation, and % deviation, making sure all numbers have the correct number of significant figures and proper units.

The density of distilled water obtained using the buret and centigram balance will be obtained by graphical methods rather than by direct calculation. The relationship between density, mass, and volume can be rearranged to a linear form, where the slope of the line is the density.

$$\frac{\text{(mass)}}{\text{(volume)}} = \text{density; multiply both sides by volume}$$

(mass) = density (volume); this is a linear relationship of the form $y = mx + b$, where y = mass, x = volume, and the slope is the density. This line should have an intercept of (0, 0).

In determining the density of the distilled water, you will construct a graph of mass (on the y-axis) versus volume (on the x-axis) for the five samples of water delivered from the buret into the plastic beaker. Be sure to follow the instructions in the appendix concerning proper graphing techniques **before** constructing your graph. A significant amount of credit will be lost for graphs which are not constructed using these guidelines.

In calculating the slope of the graph, be sure your final result has the proper units and the correct number of significant figures. Since the density of distilled water is known (see appendix of the laboratory manual), the **percent error** of your results can be calculated.

$$\text{percent error} = \frac{\text{experimental value} - \text{actual value}}{\text{actual value}} \times 100\%$$

5 Experiment

Nomenclature of Inorganic Compounds

This activity is designed to provide practice in naming inorganic compounds. **Before** coming to class, you should review the material presented in lecture and in the textbook concerning the naming of compounds. The guidelines below should be **learned**, not used as a reference in naming the compounds contained in this exercise. After reviewing the rules and practicing naming compounds and writing formulas, a nomenclature quiz will be administered.

I. Naming of Ions

a.   For simple cations (group IA, IIA, aluminum, zinc and silver), the name of the ion = name of the element + "ion."

  Ex. Zn^{2+} is called the zinc ion

b.   For simple anions (those with only one element), the name of the ion is the **root** of the name of the element ending with **ide** + "ion."

  Ex. O^{2-} **ox**ide ion, F^- **fluor**ide ion, N^{3-} **nitr**ide ion

c.   For multivalent metals (most transition metals), the charge of the metal ion must be specified.

  Ex. Fe^{3+} iron(III) ion or ferric ion

    Fe^{2+} iron(II) ion or ferrous ion

    Cu^{2+} copper(II) ion or cupric ion

You do not specify the charge for silver ion (it is always +1), zinc ion (it is always +2), or cadmium ion (always +2).

II. Naming of Binary Compounds (those with only two elements)

A. Binary Compounds Containing a Metal and Non-Metal

The name of the compound is the name of the metal followed by the name of the anion. For binary compounds containing main group metals (group IA, IIA, or IIIA), the naming is straightforward, with the name of the metal followed by the name of the ion.

Ex. NaCl is sodium chloride, Al_2O_3 is aluminum oxide

For compounds with metals of varying oxidation number or charge, you can determine the oxidation number of the metal by assigning the oxidation number to the other atoms in the compound, and making sure the net sum of all charges equals zero for a neutral compound. For such purposes, the following oxidation numbers can be assigned:

Group I (Na, Li, etc.): $+1$

Group II (Mg, Ca, etc.): $+2$

Group V (N, etc.): -3

Group VI (O, S, etc.): -2

Group VII (F, Cl, Br, etc.): -1

Ex. Name the compound $CrCl_3$. Chromium is a transition metal, and we must specify its oxidation number. In order to do this, we must know the oxidation number of the chloride ion. Chlorine is in group VII, so it has an oxidation number of -1. If three chlorides, each with a -1 charge, create a neutral compound with chromium, then Cr must have an oxidation number of $+3$.

The name of the compound is chromium(III) chloride. Other examples are:

Fe_2O_3 iron(III) oxide; Cu_2S copper(I) sulfide

B. Naming Compounds Containing Two Non-Metals

For compounds containing two non-metals, the prefixes mono, di, tri, tetra, penta, hexa, hepta, octa, etc. are used.

Ex. CO carbon monoxide; CO_2 carbon dioxide; N_2O_5 dinitrogen pentoxide

III. Naming of Polyatomic Cations and Anions

There are many complex ions which contain several atoms. You will need to learn the names of most common polyatomic ions. For cations, there are only three common ions:

NH_4^+, the ammonium ion; H_3O^+, the hydronium ion; and Hg_2^{2+}, the mercurous or mercury(I) ion.

The situation gets quite complicated for polyatomic anions. Most polyatomic anions are derived from acids (compounds which contain a removable H^+ ion) which contain hydrogen, a non-metal (such as carbon, sulfur, nitrogen, or a halogen), and oxygen. The easiest method for learning the names and formulas of all the ions is to memorize the names and formulas of the acids which they come from. To start, memorize the names and formulas of all acids with names which end in "ic." A list of common "ic" acids is provided below. To obtain the formula of the anion, remove all H^+ ions from the acid. Remember that for each H^+ ion removed, the resulting anion gets a negative charge. The name of the resulting anion will be the root name of the acid plus the ending "ate."

Acids	Anions
HNO_3 nitric acid	NO_3^- nitrate ion
$HClO_3$ chloric acid*	ClO_3^- chlorate ion*
$HClO_4$ perchloric acid*	ClO_4^- perchlorate ion*
H_2SO_4 sulfuric acid	SO_4^{2-} sulfate ion
H_3PO_4 phosphoric acid	PO_4^{3-} phosphate ion
H_2CO_3 carbonic acid	CO_3^{2-} carbonate ion

*Comparable acids and ions exist for bromine and iodine

For sulfuric, phosphoric, and carbonic acid, there are intermediate ions possible where some, but not all, of the hydrogen ions have been removed. Removal of one hydrogen ion produces the following anions.

HSO_4^- hydrogen sulfate ion (also called bisulfate ion)

$H_2PO_4^-$ dihydrogen phosphate ion

HCO_3^- hydrogen carbonate ion (also called bicarbonate ion)

If two hydrogen ions are removed from phosphoric acid. H_3PO_4, the hydrogen phosphate ion, HPO_4^{2-}, is formed.

Nitrogen, phosphorus, sulfur, chlorine, bromine, and iodine also have acids with one less oxygen atom than the "ic" acids listed above. The names of these acids end in "ous," and the anion which is formed when hydrogen ions are removed ends in "ite."

Acids	Anions
HNO_2 nitrous acid	NO_2^- nitrite ion
H_2SO_3 sulfurous acid	SO_3^{2-} sulfite ion HSO_3^- hydrogen sulfite ion or bisulfite ion
H_3PO_3 phosphorous acid	PO_3^{3-} phosphite ion HPO_3^{2-} hydrogen phosphite ion $H_2PO_3^-$ dihydrogen phosphite ion
HIO_2 iodous acid*	IO_2^- iodite ion*

* Comparable acids and ions exist for bromine and chlorine

The elements chlorine, bromine, and iodine can also exist in acids which contain two oxygens less than chloric, bromic, or iodic acid. The names of the acids and the resulting anions contain the prefix "hypo."

Ex. HBrO hypobromous acid, BrO^- hypobromite ion

There are a few other acid and ion names you need to know.

Acids	Anions
CH_3CO_2H acetic acid	$CH_3CO_2^-$ acetate ion
HCN hydrocyanic acid	CN^- cyanide ion OH^- hydroxide ion CrO_4^{2-} chromate ion $Cr_2O_7^{2-}$ dichromate ion MnO_4^- permanganate ion

Note: In learning to name compounds, you must learn both the names of the ions **and their charges**.

When naming compounds, name the cation first, followed by the name of the anion.

Ex. $Ni(HSO_4)_2$ nickel(II) hydrogen sulfate

$KClO_4$ potassium perchlorate

$Fe(NO_3)_3$ iron(III) nitrate (also called ferric nitrate)

NH_4OH ammonium hydroxide

Procedure

In this activity, you will practice naming and writing formulas for a variety of compounds. **Before** going to class, review lecture notes, the text, and the preceding pages on the naming of inorganic compounds. During the laboratory exercise, the only aides you should use are your memory and a periodic table. If you find that you have to look up the names or formulas of most of the compounds, you are not yet prepared to do this lesson.

The instructor will divide the class into several groups of three or four students. You are to work as a group on each section (one section at a time) of the nomenclature worksheet. Discussion among the members of the group is encouraged, but remember to use only your collective knowledge and a periodic table. After working on each section, the instructor will call on students, at random, to present and explain their answers. If you are in disagreement with the results of a fellow student, please ask questions to determine the correct answer and the rationale behind it. After reviewing the entire worksheet, your instructor will provide you with another problem set in nomenclature to be done on your own, in class, and turned in before you leave the laboratory.

Note: State regulations require that you wear safety glasses whenever you are in a laboratory, regardless of the activity being performed.

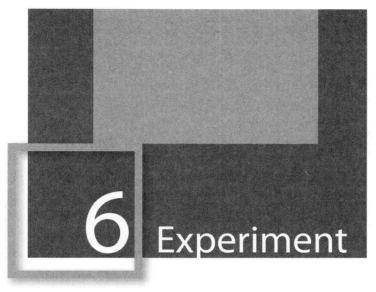

6 Experiment

Percent Composition of Carbonates

I. Introduction

Compounds containing carbonate react with hydrochloric acid to form carbon dioxide gas. This reaction is used by geologists to easily identity samples containing limestone, $CaCO_3$. A few drops of acid are placed on a sample of the rock, and if fizzing occurs (indicating the formation of CO_2 gas), the sample contains carbonate. In this experiment, samples of a carbonate-containing compound will be reacted with HCl, and by measuring the change in mass as CO_2 is liberated, the % carbonate will be determined. The reaction for calcium carbonate with hydrochloric acid is:

$$CaCO_{3(s)} + 2\,HCl_{(aq)} \rightarrow CaCl_{2(aq)} + CO_{2(g)} + H_2O_{(l)}$$

This experiment will be done in microscale, using carbonate samples of 0.50 grams or less, and 1–2 mL of HCl for each determination. Since the sample size is so small, very accurate measurements of mass will be required. All weights will be obtained using a highly sensitive electronic balance. This balance is accurate to 0.0001 g, so all objects to be weighed must be handled with lint-free tissues so that moisture from your hands does not produce an inaccurate weight. Triplicate trials will be performed on an unknown carbonate sample.

II. Equipment Needed

This experiment requires the following:

- unknown carbonate sample (from instructor)
- 3 medium-sized (100 × 13 mm) test tubes
- 1 smallest beaker

- 1 – 100 mL plastic beaker
- 1 small funnel
- 1 watch glass
- 1 micropipet with stretched tip
- 1 small funnel

III. Procedure

1. Obtain an unknown carbonate sample from your laboratory instructor. Be sure to record the unknown number on the data sheet.

2. Clean and dry three of your medium-sized (100 × 13 mm) test tubes. The reaction will be carried out in these tubes, and they must be completely dried before use.

3. Using your smallest beaker, obtain approximately 10 mL of 6 M HCl. Keep this beaker, covered with a watch glass, under the hood. **Be careful—HCl is extremely caustic.** Wash all spills thoroughly with a solution of $NaHCO_3$ followed by lots of water.

Figure 6-1.

4. Obtain a plastic micropipet with a stretched tip from your equipment drawer. Fill the micropipet with the HCl solution, invert the pipet, wipe the tip with a Kimwipe, and place the inverted pipet in a 100 mL plastic beaker. Place one of the test tubes in the beaker and weigh the beaker, test tube, and dropper containing HCl on the electronic analytical balance. (See operating instructions on the next page.) Use the same balance for all weighings. Record the mass on the data sheet.

5. Place a sample of the unknown with a mass of roughly 0.5 grams in the test tube. Use a small funnel, and be careful not to spill the sample on the outside of the test tube or inside the beaker. Tap the funnel and tube to get the sample to flow to the bottom of the test tube. After filling, wipe the test tube with a Kimwipe and place

it back in the beaker with the pipet. Reweigh the beaker with sample and acid and record the mass on the data sheet.

6.   Carefully remove the micropipet containing HCl and **slowly** add the acid to the unknown sample. Add just one drop at a time, allowing the bubbles of carbon dioxide to escape before adding another drop of acid. Continue to **slowly** add acid until there is no apparent reaction or bubbling of the sample. If the sample spatters to the walls of the test tube, use a few drops of acid to wash the sample into the bottom of the tube. The contents of the test tube can be mixed by removing the tube (handle it with Kimwipes) and gently tapping it. Be careful to not spatter any of the carbonate sample or HCl.

7.   When reaction has ceased. add the remaining acid to the test tube. Invert the dropper into the beaker and obtain the mass of the beaker, test tube, dropper, and reaction mixture. Record the mass on the data sheet.

8.   Refill the micropipet with HCl and repeat steps 4–7 two more times so that three trials are performed. After completing the third determination, return the small funnel to your instructor. Have your instructor sign your data sheet and lock your equipment drawer before leaving the laboratory.

Operation of the Electronic Analytical Balances

1.   The balance should be left on during the laboratory period. If it was accidentally switched off, turn on the balance by gently pushing down on the right side of the bar switch. Wait for the display to register all eights, four dash lines (----), and then 0.0000 g before proceeding.

2.   With the doors of the balanced closed, gently press down on the left side of the bar switch where it says "re-zero." Wait until the digital display reads "0.0000 g."

3.   Open the balance door, place the object to be weighed on the pan, close the door, and wait for a steady reading on the digital display. **Note:** Samples are always weighed in a container. Never place chemicals directly on the balance pan.

4.   After recording the mass, remove the object from the pan and close the balance doors. Use the same balance for all subsequent weighings.

IV. Calculations

During each trial, the sample should have lost a mass equal to the weight of carbon dioxide which was liberated. This makes for an easy calculation of the percent carbon dioxide, but scientists are never content with simple calculations. Instead of characterizing compounds of the type used in this experiment by their % carbon dioxide, the % carbonate is often used. Since one mole of carbon dioxide is produced for each mole of carbonate in the original compound, the amount of carbonate in the compound can be obtained by multiplying the mass of carbon dioxide by the molar mass of carbonate divided by the the molar mass of carbon dioxide. The conversion from % carbon dioxide to % carbonate is as follows:

$$\%CO_3^{2-} = \frac{\text{mass of carbonate}}{\text{mass of sample}} \times 100\%$$

$$\%CO_3^{2-} = \frac{\text{mass of } CO_2}{\text{mass of sample}} \times \frac{\text{molar mass } CO_3^{2-}}{\text{molar mass } CO_2} \times 100\%$$

You will be graded on the accuracy of the experimentally determined value of percent carbonate in your unknown. You will be required to calculate the average deviation of $\%CO_3^{2-}$ for your 3 trials, and report the average value, deviation, and average deviation of your results. The deviation of each trial is the difference between the trial result and the average result.

$$\text{deviation} = \text{trial } \% CO_3^{2-} - \text{average } \% CO_3^{2-}$$

The average deviation is the sum of the absolute values of the deviation divided by the number of trials.

$$\text{average deviation} = \frac{\text{sum of absolute values of deviation}}{\text{number of trials}}$$

7 Experiment

Formula of a Compound: Magnesium and Oxygen

I. Introduction

In this experiment you will synthesize a compound by reacting a known amount of magnesium with an excess of elemental oxygen (obtained from air). The amount of oxygen in the compound can be calculated by determining the mass of the compound after the reaction has been completed. It will have increased in mass due to the oxygen which has combined chemically with the magnesium to form the compound. By knowing the mass of both elements in the compound, it is possible to calculate the number of moles of each element in the compound. The ratio of moles of magnesium to moles of oxygen can provide the empirical formula of the compound formed.

II. Equipment Needed

This experiment requires the following:

- crucible, cover, and clay triangle (from instructor)
- tripod or ring stand and iron ring
- 2 small plastic beakers for weighing
- Bunsen burner and striker

III. Procedure

This experiment involves several very precise measurements of mass using the electronic analytical balance. To obtain good results, several precautions must be followed. Never place the object to be weighed directly on the balance pan. Place the object in a plastic beaker, weigh the beaker and the object, and then weigh the empty beaker. Also, make sure the object to be weighed has cooled to room temperature before weighing.

62

If you try to weigh it while it is still warm, you will not get a steady mass reading, and it will appear as if the object is getting heavier as it sits on the balance pan. Handle objects to be weighed with Kimwipes.

1. Obtain a crucible and cover, and a clay triangle from your laboratory instructor. Clean the crucible and cover with soap followed by rinsing with tap water and then distilled water.

2. Support the crucible and cover on a tripod or iron ring using a clay triangle, and heat the crucible and cover using a hot (blue) flame (see appendix) for 2–3 minutes. This will burn off any moisture and impurities.

3. While the crucible is cooling, obtain a few magnesium turnings. Place a clean small beaker on an electronic analytical balance and press the "zero" bar. The balance should read "0.0000g." Using Kimwipes, add pieces of magnesium to the beaker until a mass of between 0.3–0.4 grams is obtained. Record the exact mass of the magnesium on the report form.

4. Using Kimwipes, place the cooled crucible, with the cover, in a small plastic beaker and weigh it on the analytical balance. See the appendix of the lab manual and/or consult your instructor on the operation of the electronic analytical balances. Make sure all weighings are on the same balance with the same beaker. and that the balance is zeroed before each weighing. Record the weight of the crucible, cover, and beaker on the data sheet.

©Hayden-McNeil, LLC

Figure 7-1. Crucible.

5. Using Kimwipes, place the magnesium in the crucible. Place the lid on the crucible so that it is slightly tilted. Place the crucible on the clay triangle and tripod or iron ring, and place the laboratory burner under the crucible.

6. Light the burner (see the appendix and/or your instructor for directions on the operation of the burner), and heat the crucible with a moderate (not yellow and not blue) flame. If the magnesium burns or white smoke appears, quickly remove the flame and, using tongs, place the cover on the crucible. Wait a minute or two until the burning stops, and use tongs to open the crucible. Continue to heat the crucible, making sure to remove the flame and cover the crucible whenever smoking occurs. After all smoking has ceased, heat the crucible, with the cover tilted, using an intense flame (see appendix) for an additional 8–10 minutes. After heating, allow the crucible to cool to room temperature (at least 10 minutes).

Note: Some of the magnesium may have reacted with nitrogen in the air to produce magnesium nitride. To convert magnesium nitride to magnesium oxide:

7. Carefully add 10 drops of distilled water to the crucible using an eyedropper. Make sure all of the white powder stays inside the crucible.

8. Place the crucible, with lid ajar, on the tripod or iron ring, and gently heat for 5 minutes. After 5 minutes of gentle heating, heat with an intense flame for an additional 5 minutes.

9. Allow the crucible and contents to cool to room temperature (at least 10 minutes). After cooling, using Kimwipes, place the cooled crucible, with the cover, in the plastic beaker previously used for weighing, and weigh the beaker, crucible, cover, and product on the electronic balance. Record the mass on the data sheet.

10. Repeat steps 8–9 until two weighings agree within 0.0008 grams. Use the last weight obtained in your calculations.

11. Wash the contents of the crucible down the sink, and flush with tap water. Clean and dry the crucible and cover.

12. Return the crucible, cover, and clay triangle to your instructor and have your data sheet signed and equipment drawer locked before leaving the laboratory.

IV. Calculations

The experimental or empirical formula of the product formed from the reaction of magnesium and oxygen will be determined. Keep in mind that although you may know the formula of the compound formed between magnesium and oxygen, the experimental conditions can affect the outcome of a chemical reaction. The white smoke which may have formed is magnesium oxide, and some of it may have escaped from the crucible. Also, if the procedure is not carefully followed, magnesium nitride may have formed instead of magnesium oxide. As a result, your experimental results may not result in an "ideal" formula.

The number of moles of magnesium can be calculated from the mass of magnesium before the reaction took place. The mass of the product will include both the mass of magnesium plus the mass of oxygen reacted. Subtraction of the mass of the magnesium gives the mass of oxygen reacted. From this mass, the number of moles of oxygen in the compound can be calculated.

The empirical formula can be obtained by determining the ratio of moles of magnesium atoms combined with one mole of oxygen atoms. The empirical formula is this ratio expressed in simple whole numbers.

The % Mg of your product will be used in assigning part of your grade for this experiment. It is calculated as follows:

$$\% \, Mg = \frac{\text{mass of magnesium}}{\text{mass of compound}} \times 100\%$$

The experimental value of % Mg can be compared to the theoretical value of % Mg based on the actual formula of magnesium oxide. Use the atomic weight of magnesium and the molar mass of magnesium oxide to calculate the theoretical % Mg. You can calculate the percent error in your results by comparing the experimental % Mg with the theoretical % Mg as follows.

$$\% \text{ error} = \frac{\text{experimental value} - \text{theoretical value}}{\text{theoretical value}} \times 100\%$$

8 Experiment

Spectrophotometric Determination of the Formula of a Complex Ion

I. Introduction

In this experiment you will determine the formula of a complex ion using an instrument called a spectrophotometer. A *complex ion* is an ion containing a central metal ion which is bonded to one or more molecules or ions. The complex ion you will be studying is colored, and a *spectrophotometer* is a device which can be used to measure the intensity of colors.

The reaction between the iron(III) ion and an organic molecule called 5-sulfosalicylic acid (abbreviated as SSA) will be studied. The iron(III) ion is colorless, 5-sulfosalicylic acid is colorless, and the product formed is purple in color. You will make a series of solutions which combine various amounts of iron(III) ion with varying amounts of 5-sulfosalicylic acid. In some of the solutions there will be an excess of iron(III), in others there will be an excess of SSA. When enough SSA has been added to fully react with all of the iron(III) present in the solution, a maximum amount of the product will form, and the solution will reach a purple color of maximum intensity. Rather than using your eye to detect the color intensity of the product, you will use a spectrophotometer to measure the color intensity. Your measurements will be treated graphically to determine the formula of the product made from combining iron(III) ion and 5-sulfosalicylic acid.

The reaction to be studied is:

$$Fe^{3+}(aq) \quad + \quad x \quad \text{(5-sulfosalicylic acid)} \quad \longrightarrow \quad [Fe(SSA)x]^{3+}(aq)$$

(colorless)   5-sulfosalicylic acid   (purple)

Figure 8-1. 5-sulfosalicylic acid.

The corners of the hexagonal ring in the structure of 5-sulfosalicylic acid represent carbons with hydrogen atoms attached. The lone pairs of electrons on the oxygen atoms are capable of bonding to the iron(III) ion to form the product.

You will determine the value of X for this reaction by mixing various amounts of SSA with varying amounts of iron(III) and measuring the intensity of the color of the product using the spectrophotometer. Your data will be graphed to determine the value of X. Since X is the number of 5-sulfosalicylic acid molecules needed to react with a single iron(III) ion, it should be a small whole number.

The Theory of Spectroscopy

Substances which are colored absorb electromagnetic radiation in the visible region. The wavelength (or color) of the radiation absorbed depends on the chemical nature of the substance. In this experiment, the absorption of radiation by a colored complex ion will be examined using an instrument called a spectrophotometer. A spectrophotometer can measure the intensity of electromagnetic radiation at various wavelengths. In the visible range, the wavelength at which a given substance absorbs the maximum amount of radiation is directly related to the color of the substance. For example, substances which appear blue in color absorb light with wavelengths from 580–600 nanometers (nm, equal to 10^{-9} meters) and substances which appear red in color absorb light with wavelengths of approximately 490 nm. Most pure substances have a specific wavelength at which they absorb a maximum amount of radiation. This wavelength is called λ_{max}, where λ (lambda) is the symbol for wavelength, and max stands for maximum absorbance of radiation. For most colored substances, the extent to which light at λ_{max} is absorbed is directly related to how many molecules of the substance are present. That is, samples which contain high concentrations of a colored substance will absorb more radiation at λ_{max} than more dilute samples of the same substance. This relationship, called the Beer–Lambert law, has been used to determine the concentrations of very dilute samples of substances.

In order to use the Beer–Lambert relationship between absorbance of radiation and concentration, some terms must be defined. The liquid sample is placed in a special test tube or cell, and exposed to light of the appropriate wavelength. The intensity of the radiation entering the cell is compared to the intensity of the radiation leaving the cell. The amount of radiation absorbed by the sample will depend on the nature of the substance, the concentration of the sample, and the length of the path of light as it travels through the cell.

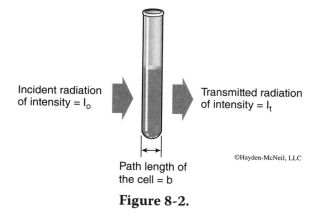

Incident radiation of intensity = I_o

Transmitted radiation of intensity = I_t

Path length of the cell = b

©Hayden-McNeil, LLC

Figure 8-2.

The absorbance of the sample, A, is related to the path length, concentration and nature of the substance by the following equation.

$$A = \varepsilon bc = \log (I_o/I_t)$$

Where

> A = absorbance, and can be obtained from the spectrophotometer

> ε = molar absorbtivity or molar extinction coefficient, and depends on the nature of the substance

> c = molarity of the absorbing substance

The fraction I_o/I_t is defined as the transmittance. The percent transmittance (%T) is $I_t/I_o \times 100\%$, and can be read directly from the scale on the spectrophotometer. Since the %T scale is linear and the absorbance scale is logarithmic, it is easier to read % transmittance and convert it to absorbance as follows.

$$A = \varepsilon bc = \log (100/\%T) = 2 - \log \%T$$

If the same cell is used for all measurements, then b, the path length, is constant. Likewise, ε, extinction coefficient, is constant for a given substance. Thus, the absorbance at λ_{max} of the solutions you prepare will be directly proportional to the concentration of the iron(III)-SSA product. When the ratio of SSA to iron(III) is such that a maximum amount of product is formed, the absorbance will reach a maximum.

II. Equipment Needed

This experiment requires the following:

- 9 – 125 × 15 mm (medium) test tubes
- 10 mL graduated pipet and rubber bulb (from instructor)
- small beaker
- large waste beaker
- 2 – 100 mL beakers
- test tube rack
- Kimwipes

III. Procedure

1. Using two clean, dry 100 mL beakers, obtain 60 mL each of the Fe(III) stock solution and the 5-sulfosalicylic acid (SSA) stock solution. Record the exact concentrations of each solution on your data sheet.

2. Obtain a 10 mL graduated (Mohr) pipet, and clean it and nine 125 × 15 mm (medium) sized test tubes. Rinse first with soap, then with tap water, and finally with distilled water. Dry the test tubes.

3. Pour approximately 10 mL of the iron(III) stock solution into a small beaker and rinse the pipet three times by drawing up 2–3 mL of the solution using the rubber pipet bulb. Discard the rinsings in the sink. Pipet exactly the following volumes of the stock iron(III) solution into each of the nine test tubes.

Test Tube #	mL Fe(III) Stock Solution
1	1.00
2	2.00
3	3.00
4	4.00
5	5.00
6	6.00
7	7.00
8	8.00
9	9.00

4. Rinse the pipet by drawing up several 2–3 mL portions of distilled water using the rubber pipet bulb, discarding the rinsings in the sink. Transfer approximately 10 mL of the SSA stock solution into a small beaker and rinse the pipet by drawing up several 2–3 mL samples of the solution and discarding the rinsings in the sink.

5. After rinsing the pipet with the 5-sulfosalicylic acid solution, pipet the following volumes into each of the test tubes.

Test Tube #	mL SSA Stock Solution
1	9.00
2	8.00
3	7.00
4	6.00
5	5.00
6	4.00
7	3.00
8	2.00
9	1.00

6. Stir all solutions thoroughly using a glass rod. Be sure to wipe off the rod before transferring it to a new test tube. After mixing, bring the test tube rack, Kimwipes, a waste beaker, your lab manual, and a pen to the Spectronic 20.

7. Follow the instructions in the appendix for setting the Spectronic 20 to 0 and 100% transmittance. Set the wavelength to 505 nm. Use distilled water in the solvent cell when setting the instrument to 100% transmittance.

©Hayden-McNeil, LLC

Figure 8-3. Line up the white etch mark with the line on the cell holder.

8. When inserting the special cells (called cuvettes) into the sample holder, make sure the etching on the cell lines up with the mark on the holder. The cell should be filled only half way. Be sure to wipe the outside with a Kimwipe and to handle the cell on the top half only.

9. Starting with solution #1, use a small portion of the solution to rinse the Spectronic 20 solution cell. Fill the cell half way with the solution, wipe the outside of the cell with a Kimwipe, and insert it in the cell holder. Read and record the % transmittance of the solution on the data sheet. When making measurements, stand directly in front of the meter to avoid parallax. Use the mirror on the scale to be sure you are standing in the proper position. The reflection of the needle should be obscured by the needle when you are in the correct position.

10. Discard the contents of the cell in the waste beaker, and repeat the rinsing, filling, and wiping of the cell with solution #2. Read and record the % transmittance of the solution and repeat this step with solutions 3–9.

11. After making all measurements, rinse the solution cell with distilled water, and make sure both the solution cell and the solvent cell are placed in the rack next to the spectrophotometer. Discard the contents of the waste beaker in the sink.

12. Have your instructor lock your equipment drawer and sign your data sheet before leaving the laboratory.

IV. Calculations

The formula of the complex ion formed between the iron(III) ion and 5-sulfosalicylic acid will be determined graphically by plotting the absorbance of each solution versus the mole fraction of 5-sulfosalicylic acid for each of the nine solutions. The absorbance of each solution can be calculated from the measured percent transmittance using the equation:

$$A = \log(100/\%T) = 2 - \log\%T$$

When taking the logarithm of a number, the resulting log should have as many places after the decimal as significant figures in the original number. For example, a sample with a % transmittance of 26.3 (3 significant figures) has an absorbance of:

$$Abs = 2 - \log 26.3 = 2 - 1.420 = 0.580 \text{ (3 places after the decimal)}$$

The mole fraction of SSA (X_{SSA}) is defined as:

$$\text{mole fraction SSA } (= X_{SSA}) = \frac{\text{moles SSA}}{\text{moles SSA} + \text{moles Fe(III)}}$$

where moles SSA = Volume $_{SSA \text{ stock solution}}$ (in liters) $\times$ M$_{SSA}$ stock soln, and moles Fe(III) = Volume $_{Fe(III)}$ stock solution (in liters) $\times$ M$_{Fe(III)}$ stock soln.

The mole fraction of Fe(III) can be calculated by subtracting X_{SSA} from 1, since X_{SSA} + $X_{Fe(III)}$ = 1.00.

The mole fraction of SSA is calculated and graphed along the x-axis, with absorbance graphed along the y-axis. Such a graph should be similar to Figure 8-4 (for a copper(II)-ammonia product), and show two linear segments.

The first linear segment of your graph should show the absorbance of the solution (i.e., the concentration of the colored product) increasing as the ratio of SSA to iron(III) approaches the stoichiometric amount. As the mole fraction of SSA increases above the stoichiometric amount (excess SSA and not enough iron(III) to react with it), the absorbance of the solution decreases in a linear fashion. The point of intersection of these linear segments is used to determine the formula of the complex ion formed.

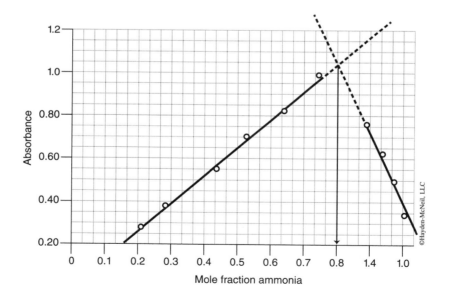

Figure 8-4. Graph of absorbance vs. mole fraction ammonia with respect to copper(II).

On the previous page is a sample graph for a product formed between copper(II) ion and ammonia. Note that the two linear sections of the graph are extended to the point where they intersect. The graph shows that the two lines intersect at a mole fraction of ammonia equal to 0.80. This corresponds to a mole fraction of copper(II) equal to $1.00 - .80 = 0.20$. The formula of the complex ion has a mole ratio of ammonia to copper equal to $.80 \div .20 = 4.0$. This indicates that the correct formula for the product formed between copper(II) and ammonia is $Cu(NH_3)_4^{2+}$.

In this experiment, you will make a comparable graph to determine the formula of the complex ion formed between iron(III) and 5-sulfosalicylic acid. Be sure to follow the graphing instructions in the appendix and to determine the intersection point of the two linear segments of the graph as explained above.

Once the intersection point of the two lines has been determined graphically, the formula of the complex ion can be determined by figuring out the whole number ratio of one reactant to the other. In this experiment, you will graphically obtain the mole fraction of 5-sulfosalicylic acid and mole fraction of iron(III) which produces the highest concentration of product (maximum absorbance). Divide the mole fraction of SSA by the mole fraction of iron(III) to determine the moles SSA/mole Fe(III) in the product. You may need to round this ratio to the nearest whole number to obtain the actual formula of the product.

9 Experiment

Heats of Reaction and Hess' Law

I. Introduction

This experiment is designed to measure the amount of heat lost or gained as chemical changes occur. This is accomplished by conducting chemical reactions in an insulated reaction vessel called a *calorimeter*. If the heat capacity (amount of heat absorbed per 1° change in temperature) of both the calorimeter and the solutions it contains are known, then the change in temperature measured during the reaction can be used to calculate the *heat of reaction*, ΔH.

The general procedure for the measurement of heat change is to react known amounts of solutions, and measure their temperatures before and after they are mixed. Knowing the heat capacities of the solutions, the mass of each solution, and the temperature change enables one to calculate the change in heat due to the mixing or reaction. The calculations are outlined in Section IV.

Heat capacities of aqueous solutions are known or easily determined, but the heat capacity of the calorimeter must be determined experimentally. The calorimeter consists of two nested styrofoam cups. Although it is not a perfect insulator, results should be good enough to provide reasonably accurate results for the heats of reaction which are to be measured. The heat capacity of the calorimeter, C_{cal}, is the amount of heat absorbed by the calorimeter walls and by the thermometer per degree change in temperature. The heat capacity of a calorimeter such as those used in this experiment has been previously determined.

It is very important that you use the same calorimeter for all reactions.

II. Equipment Needed

This experiment requires the following:

- styrofoam cups calorimeter (from instructor)
- 0.1°C thermometer (from instructor)
- ring stand and iron ring
- 100 mL plastic beaker
- 400 mL glass beaker
- Kimwipes
- 2 small beakers
- 50 mL graduated cylinder
- a watch with a second hand

III. Procedure

You will be working with a very expensive mercury thermometer which has 0.1°C scale divisions. These thermometers are very delicate, and should be treated gently. Mercury is toxic, so report all breakage to your laboratory instructor. When in use, the thermometer should be supported using a ring stand and iron ring as illustrated on the next page. All temperature readings using these thermometers should be to the nearest tenth of a degree.

1. Obtain one set of styrofoam cups, a cover, and one 0.1°C thermometer from your laboratory instructor. Set up a ring stand and iron ring to support the thermometer as illustrated. The set of styrofoam cups and cover will serve as the calorimeter.

2. Only plastic beakers and styrofoam cups are to come in contact with the thermometer, so as to minimize breakage. When in use, the upper end of the thermometer should be supported using an iron ring, and the styrofoam cups should be placed in a 400 mL glass beaker.

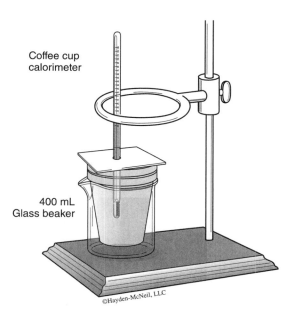

Coffee cup
calorimeter

400 mL
Glass beaker

©Hayden-McNeil, LLC

Figure 9-1. Always use a ring stand and iron ring to support the thermometer.

A. Heat of Neutralization of HCl and NaOH

1. Be sure to use the same set of cups and the same thermometer throughout all parts of the procedure. Place 50.0 mL of aqueous HCl in a plastic 100 mL beaker, and place 50.0 mL of aqueous NaOH in the calorimeter. Record the exact concentration of both solutions on the data sheet.

2. Cover the calorimeter and record the temperature of both solutions every minute for three minutes as follows. Measure the temperature of the NaOH in the calorimeter (to the nearest 0.1°C) and carefully remove the thermometer. Wipe the end with a Kimwipe before placing the thermometer in the beaker of HCl. Hold the thermometer while it is in the beaker of acid and measure and record the temperature. After measuring the temperature, remove the thermometer, wipe the tip with a Kimwipe, and place it back in the calorimeter supported by the ring. Repeat this step two more times at 1-minute intervals. Always wipe the tip of the thermometer with a Kimwipe when changing solutions. Make sure the thermometer is supported (by the ring stand or your hand) at all times. At the fourth minute, quickly add the HCl to the NaOH in the calorimeter. Slide the lid closed, and record the temperature in the calorimeter every minute for three minutes.

3. After all readings have been made and recorded, empty the contents of the cups in the sink and repeat steps 1–2 for a second trial.

B. Heat of Reaction of Mg and HCl

1. Label two small beakers, and, using the analytical balance, weigh and record their weights.

2. Place approximately 0.25 grams of magnesium in each beaker and reweigh on the analytical balance. The sample should have a weight of 0.24–0.26 g. Record the exact weights of each sample on the data sheet.

3. Place 50 mL of aqueous HCl in the clean, dry calorimeter. Cover the calorimeter and record the temperature every minute for three minutes. Make sure the thermometer is supported (by the ring stand or your hand) at all times. At the fourth minute, quickly add one of the Mg samples to the HCl in the calorimeter. Slide the lid closed, and record the temperature in the calorimeter every minute for three minutes.

4. It is difficult to determine the final temperature due to the time it takes for a reaction to occur. Continue recording temperatures until you reach a maximum temperature. Record this maximum temperature, and use it for further calculations as described below. Discard the contents of the calorimeter in the sink.

5. Clean and dry the calorimeter and repeat steps 3 and 4 using the second sample of magnesium.

C. Heat of Solution of Potassium Bromide

In this procedure, you will determine the heat absorbed or evolved when a solid salt is dissolved in water.

1. Using a small beaker and a triple beam balance, place approximately 5 grams of KBr in the beaker, weigh, and record the mass on your data sheet.

2. Using a graduated cylinder, measure 50.0 mL of distilled water (at room temperature) and place it in the calorimeter. With the lid and thermometer in place, record the temperature at 1-minute intervals for three minutes.

3. At the next interval, slide the lid up and add the contents of the small beaker to the calorimeter. Gently swirl the mixture and **carefully** stir the contents with the thermometer to make the salt dissolve as quickly as possible. Record the temperature of the mixture every minute for the next three minutes. Continue mixing.

4. It is difficult to determine the final temperature due to the time it takes to dissolve the salt. Continue mixing and recording temperatures until you reach a minimum temperature. Record this minimum temperature, and use it for further calculations as described on the following page. Discard the contents of the calorimeter in the sink. Weigh the small beaker on the triple beam balance and record the weight on the data sheet.

5. Repeat steps 1–4 above for a second determination.

6. Empty and wash the styrofoam cup. Rinse off the thermometer and gently dry it with Kimwipes. Return all special equipment to your instructor. Have your instructor sign your data sheet and lock your equipment drawer before leaving the laboratory.

Note: The calculations and preparations of graphs required for the laboratory report are quite time-consuming. Start work on the report well in advance of the due date as late laboratory reports will not be accepted and failure to produce graphs according to the procedures outlined in the appendix will result in a large grade penalty.

IV. Calculations

For each reaction, you will be required to calculate the heat liberated or absorbed per mole of reactant or product. In order to do this, you must know the temperature change of the reaction mixture, the specific heat of the reaction mixture (the number of joules needed to raise the temperature of one gram of the mixture by 1°C), and the amount of heat absorbed by the calorimeter and thermometer (the heat capacity). The heat capacity of a typical styrofoam cup calorimeter has been determined to be 41.7 joules/°C. This quantity, C_{cal}, is the amount of heat absorbed by the calorimeter walls and the thermometer with each 1°C rise in temperature.

All calculations for this experiment involve the same basic equation:

$$V_{soln} \text{ (mL)} \times \delta_{soln} \text{ (g/mL)} \times \text{specific heat (joule/g°C)} \times \Delta T \text{ (°C)}$$
$$= \text{heat change (in joules)}$$

where: δ is the density of the solution
ΔT is the temperature change $= T_{final} - T_{initial}$

The change in temperature of the reaction mixtures is the difference between the temperature of each solution at the time of mixing compared to the temperature of the reaction mixture at mixing. Since the temperature at the instant of mixing is impossible to measure, ΔT is obtained graphically. You will need to prepare graphs of temperature versus time for Parts A, B, and C of the experiment. You should use mm grid paper, and follow all the instructions for graphing contained in the appendix. Use a scale so that 1 mm = 0.1°C. It is important to draw, **using a straight edge**, the **best straight line** through the data points to obtain the correct change in temperature.

For the neutralization reaction in Part A, your graph may look similar to Figure 9-2. The initial temperatures of the two solutions (which have been sitting at room temperature for quite some time) are probably the same. If your data shows the two solutions to be at different temperatures prior to mixing, you can graph the average temperature of the solutions versus time to obtain ΔT.

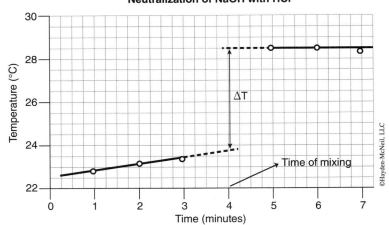

Figure 9-2. Graph of temperature versus time for the neutralization of NaOH with HCl.

The heat given off by the reaction (assuming it is exothermic) is used to warm the contents of the calorimeter (the solutions) and the calorimeter itself. The heat given off by the reaction is therefore equal to the heat absorbed by the solution and the calorimeter.

To calculate the heat of reaction, the equation below should be used.

$$\text{Heat of reaction} + \text{heat change of solutions} + C_{cal}\Delta T_{cal} = 0$$

where

$$C_{cal} \text{ is the heat capacity of the calorimeter} = 41.7 \text{ J/°C}$$

$$\Delta T_{cal} \text{ is the temperature change of the calorimeter} = T_{final} - T_{initial}$$
$$\text{(obtained from your graph)}$$

Since NaOH always remains in the calorimeter, the temperature change of NaOH equals the temperature change of the calorimeter. The heat capacity of the calorimeter has already been determined to be 41.7 joule/°C. The general equation below can be used to solve for the heat change the solutions in the calorimeter.

$$V_{soln} \text{ (mL)} \times \delta_{soln} \text{ (g/mL)} \times \text{specific heat (joule/g°C)} \times \Delta T \text{ (°C)}$$

$$= \text{heat change of the solutions (in joules)}$$

where:

$$\delta \text{ is the density of the solution } (= 1.02 \text{ g/mL})$$

$$\Delta T \text{ is the temperature change} = T_{final} - T_{initial}$$

$$\text{specific heat} = 3.93 \text{ joules/g°C}$$

For the acid–base neutralization, keep in mind that the volume of solution is the **total** volume of both solutions. Assume a density of 1.02 g/mL for the HCl and NaOH solutions, and a specific heat of 3.93 joules/g°C for the neutralization products.

Using the previous equation, solve for the heat change of the solutions. The heat change of the solutions plus the heat change of the calorimeter ($C_{cal}\Delta T$) will be equal to the total heat of reaction.

Make sure to pay attention to the signs of the heat changes. For exothermic reactions, ΔH is negative. For endothermic reactions, it is positive. Make sure you include the correct sign when reporting heats of reaction or heats of solution in your lab report.

Heats of reaction are generally reported in molar quantities rather than for specific reaction conditions. Once you calculate the heat of reaction, you must divide by the number of moles of product formed from the neutralization reaction. Determine the number of moles of acid and base reacted by using the exact volumes and molarities.

$$V \text{ (in liters)} \times M \text{ (moles/liter)} = \text{\# of moles}$$

Determine the limiting reagent, and divide the heat of reaction by the number of moles of limiting reagent to calculate the molar heat of neutralization.

For Part B, you should determine the temperature of the solution at mixing (time = 4.00 minutes) graphically by extrapolation. Use this temperature as $T_{initial}$, and use the maximum temperature reached as T_{final}. Determine if magnesium or HCl is the limiting reagent, and report the heat of reaction per mole of magnesium reacted. Assume the same density and specific heat for reactant and product solutions as in Part A.

For Part C, you should determine the temperature of the solution at mixing (time = 4.00 minutes) graphically by extrapolation. Use this temperature as $T_{initial}$, and use the minimum temperature reached as T_{final}.

$$\text{Heat of solution} + \text{heat change of contents} + \text{heat change of calorimeter} = 0$$
$$\text{Heat of solution} + (V \times \delta \times \text{specific heat} \times \Delta T) + C_{cal}\Delta T = 0$$

where:

$$V = \text{volume of solution (50.0 mL)}$$

$$\delta = \text{density of solution (assume 1.02 g/mL)}$$

$$\text{specific heat} = 3.93 \text{ joules/g°C}$$

$$C_{cal} = \text{heat capacity of calorimeter}$$

$$\Delta T = \text{temperature change} = T_{final} - T_{initial}$$

The heat of solution calculated above is for the specific amount of salt you dissolved. Use the molar mass of the salt (including waters of hydration) and the mass of salt dissolved to calculate the molar heat of solution of the salt.

V. Reports

Your laboratory report should include all data, sample calculations and results as specified on the data/report sheets. All sample calculations should include the general formula used, and show all units. You need only show the calculations for one trial when repeat trials were performed.

All data should be graphed according to the general graphing procedures in the appendix. Be sure to use mm grid paper. Choose a vertical scale so that 1 mm is equal to 0.1°C. Failure to follow these instructions will result in substantial grade penalties. Your report should include 6 graphs:

a. Temperature versus time for Part A—two trials

b. Temperature versus time for Part B—two trials

c. Temperature versus time for Part C—two trials

[Report Form]

Name	Section #

Instructor's Signature	Date

I. Data

Record data in ink, with units and the correct number of significant figures.

A. Neutralization of HCl and NaOH

1. Concentration of reagents: NaOH _____ HCl _____

2. Temperature of Solutions

    Trial 1

Time	NaOH	HCl
1.00	_____	_____
2.00	_____	_____
3.00	_____	_____
4.00	solutions are mixed	
5.00	_____	
6.00	_____	
7.00	_____	

    Trial 2

Time	NaOH	HCl
1.00	_____	_____
2.00	_____	_____
3.00	_____	_____
4.00	solutions are mixed	
5.00	_____	
6.00	_____	
7.00	_____	

B. Reaction of Mg and HCl

1. Concentration of reagents: HCl _____

2. Mass Data

	Trial 1	Trial 2
a. mass of beaker + Mg	_____	_____
b. mass of beaker	_____	_____

3. Temperature of HCl and Reaction Mixture

Time	Trial 1	Trial 2
1.00	_____	_____
2.00	_____	_____
3.00	_____	_____
4.00	add magnesium to HCl	
5.00	_____	
6.00	_____	
7.00	_____	

Maximum temperature reached: Trial 1 _____ Trial 2 _____

C. Heat of Solution

1. Formula of salt _____

2. Mass Data

	Trial 1	Trial 2
a. mass of beaker + salt	_____	_____
b. mass of beaker	_____	_____

3. Temperature of Water and Reaction Mixture

Time	Trial 1	Trial 2
1.00	_____	_____
2.00	_____	_____
3.00	_____	_____
4.00	add salt to water	
5.00	_____	
6.00	_____	
7.00	_____	

Minimum temperature reached: Trial 1 _____ Trial 2 _____

[Report Form continued]

Name _____ Section # _____

II. Calculations

Show a sample for Trial 1 where requested.

A. Neutralization of HCl and NaOH

1. Temperature from graphs:

	Trial 1	Trial 2
NaOH and HCl at time of mixing	_____	_____
Reaction mixture at time of mixing	_____	_____

2. Heat change of mixed solutions—sample calculation
   $[= V_{soln} \times \delta_{soln} \times$ specific heat $\times \Delta T]$

   Results: Trial 1 _____ Trial 2 _____

3. Heat change of calorimeter—sample calculation: Trial 1 $[= (C_{cal})(\Delta T_{cal})]$

   Results: Trial 1 _____ Trial 2 _____

4. Heat of reaction—sample calculation: Trial 1
[Heat of reaction + heat change of solutions + $C_{cal}\Delta T_{cal} = 0$]

Results: Trial 1 _____ Trial 2 _____

5. Moles of limiting reagent—sample calculation

Results: _____

6. Molar Heat of Neutralization (per mole of water formed)
(show calculation—Trial 1)

Results: Trial 1 _____ Trial 2 _____ Average _____

B. Reaction of Mg and HCl

1. Temperatures:

	Trial 1	Trial 2
HCl at time of mixing (from graphs)	_____	_____
Reaction mixture (maximum temperature)	_____	_____

[Report Form continued]

Name _____ Section # _____

2. Heat change of reaction mixture—sample calculation: Trial 1
    $[= V_{soln} \times \delta_{soln} \times \text{specific heat} \times \Delta T]$

    Results: Trial 1 _____ Trial 2 _____

3. Heat change of calorimeter—sample calculation: Trial 1
    $[= (C_{cal})(\Delta T_{cal})]$

    Results: Trial 1 _____ Trial 2 _____

4. Heat of reaction—sample calculation: Trial 1
    [Heat of reaction + heat change of reaction mixture + $C_{cal} \Delta T_{cal} = 0$]

    Results: Trial 1 _____ Trial 2 _____

5. Moles of limiting reagent—show calculation

Results: _____

6. Molar Heat of Reaction (per mole of Mg reacted)
   sample calculation: Trial 1

Results: Trial 1 _____ Trial 2 _____ Average _____

C. Heat of Solution

1. Formula of salt _____

2. Mass of salt dissolved   **Trial 1**   **Trial 2**
                                            _____   _____

3. Moles of salt dissolved—sample calculation: Trial 1

Results: Trial 1 _____ Trial 2 _____

[Report Form continued]

Name _____ Section # _____

4. Temperature of solution at mixing (from graph extrapolated to time = 4.00 minutes)

   Results: Trial 1 _____ Trial 2 _____

5. ΔT from minimum temperature reached after mixing and temperature of solution at mixing (item 4).

   Results: Trial 1 _____ Trial 2 _____

6. Heat change of solution—sample calculation: w
   [$= V \times \delta \times$ specific heat $\times \Delta T$]

   Results: Trial 1 _____ Trial 2 _____

7. Heat change of calorimeter—sample calculation: Trial 1
   [$= C_{cal}\Delta T$]

   Results: Trial 1 _____ Trial 2 _____

8. Total heat of solution—sample calculation: Trial 1

[Heat of solution + heat change of contents + heat change of calorimeter = 0]

Results: Trial 1 _____ Trial 2 _____

9. Molar heat of solution—sample calculation: Trial 1

Results: Trial 1 _____ Trial 2 _____ Average _____

III. Tabulation of Results—Molar Heats of Reaction

		Trial 1	Trial 2	Average	Avg. Dev.
a.	NaOH and HCl	_____	_____	_____	_____
b.	Mg and HCl	_____	_____	_____	_____
c.	Salt: _____	_____	_____	_____	_____

*deviation is: trial value − average value

average deviation is: $\dfrac{\text{sum of absolute values of deviation}}{\text{number of trials}}$

Attach all 6 graphs to the laboratory report. Follow the graphing instructions in the appendix of the manual and make sure each graph has your name and section # on it.

[Report Form continued]

Name _____   Section # _____

IV. Questions

1. The accepted value for the heat of neutralization of NaOH with HCl is −56.2 kJ/mole. Compare this with your average experimental value and calculate the % error in your results.

$$\% \ error = \frac{accepted \ value - experimental \ value}{accepted \ value} \times 100\%$$

2. a. Write the net ionic equation and your experimental value of $\Delta H_{neutralization}$ from Part A of the experiment.

   b. Write the net ionic equation for the reaction of magnesium with acid and your experimental value of $\Delta H_{reaction}$ from Part B of the experiment.

c. Using the previous equations and heats of reaction, apply Hess' Law to obtain ΔH for the following reaction of magnesium with water.

$$Mg_{(s)} + 2\,H_2O_{(l)} \rightarrow Mg(OH)_{2\ (aq)} + H_{2(g)}$$

10 Experiment

The Atomic Weight of a Metal

I. Introduction

In this experiment, the gram-atomic mass of zinc or magnesium will be determined by measuring the amount of hydrogen gas produced by the reaction of the metal with hydrochloric acid.

$$Zn_{(s)} + 2\,HCl_{(aq)} \rightarrow ZnCl_{2(aq)} + H_{2(g)}$$

$$Mg_{(s)} + 2\,HCl_{(aq)} \rightarrow MgCl_{2(aq)} + H_{2(g)}$$

Three weighed samples of metal will be reacted with an excess of concentrated hydrochloric acid. The volume, temperature, and pressure of the hydrogen gas produced will be determined, and the ideal gas law used to calculate the moles of hydrogen produced. Using the stoichiometry of the above reactions, the number of moles of metal reacted can be obtained, and the gram-atomic weight of the metal can be calculated.

II. Equipment Needed

This experiment requires the following:

- gas measuring tube and stopper assembly (from instructor)
- metal samples (from instructor)
- small beaker
- Kimwipes
- 500–600 mL beaker

- ring stand and clamp

- funnel

- Bunsen burner, iron ring, striker, and wire gauze (if assigned to work with zinc)

III. Procedure

1. Obtain a gas measuring tube and stopper assembly from your laboratory instructor. The gas measuring tubes are quite expensive, so be very careful when cleaning and filling them. Clean the tube thoroughly with soap solution, and rinse with tap water and then distilled water.

2. Fill a 500–600 mL beaker with 2–3 inches of water.

3. Obtain three samples of the same metal from your laboratory instructor. Be sure to handle the metal sample with Kimwipes. If you are using zinc, you will need to heat approximately 300 mL of distilled water to a temperature of approximately 30°C. Set up a tripod (or ring stand and ring) with wire gauze and a Bunsen burner, and start heating the water.

4. Weigh a sample of the metal, in a small beaker, on the electronic balance. See the appendix and/or consult your instructor on the operation of the analytical balances. Record the mass of the beaker plus sample, and the mass of the empty beaker on the data sheet. For zinc, the sample mass should be no greater than 0.250 grams. For magnesium, the sample mass should be no greater than 0.080 grams. If your sample exceeds these limits, break off a small piece of the metal or obtain another sample from your instructor.

5. The stopper for the gas measuring tube has a piece of copper wire on it. Wrap this wire around your weighed metal sample several times, so that the sample is securely attached to the stopper.

6. Clamp the gas tube to a ring stand with the closed end toward the floor and the open end toward the ceiling. Place a funnel in the open end of the tube, and very carefully add 10.0 mL of 6.0 M HCl.

   Note: Hydrochloric acid is extremely caustic. Clean up all spills by first washing with a solution of sodium bicarbonate and then rinsing thoroughly with water.

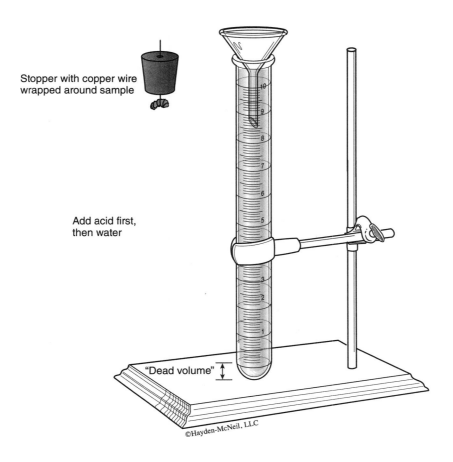

Stopper with copper wire wrapped around sample

Add acid first, then water

"Dead volume"

©Hayden-McNeil, LLC

Figure 10-1. Stopper with copper wire wrapped around sample.

Note: Usually acid is added to water, rather than the other way around. In this procedure the acid is placed in the tube first so that the tube can be inverted safely, without acid running out the bottom while you are placing the inverted tube in the beaker of water.

7. Examine the closed end of the tube. Although the tube is graduated in tenths of a milliliter, the closed end may contain a "dead space" where the volume is not calibrated. When filling the tube with distilled water, be sure to leave a large enough amount of air so that you can obtain an initial and final volume reading for the hydrogen produced. Fill the tube (leaving enough air for the uncalibrated space at the bottom) with either:

    For zinc: water at 25–30°C or

    For magnesium: water at approximately 20°C

8. **Gently** place the stopper in the top of the tube; **do not force it**. Cover the hole in the stopper with your finger and invert the tube into the large beaker of water and clamp it in place as shown in Figure 10-2. Once clamped in place, take an initial volume reading **before** the reaction starts. Record the initial volume on the data sheet, estimating to the hundredth of a milliliter.

The acid, which is more dense than water, will quickly sink and diffuse downward and react with the metal, producing bubbles of hydrogen gas.

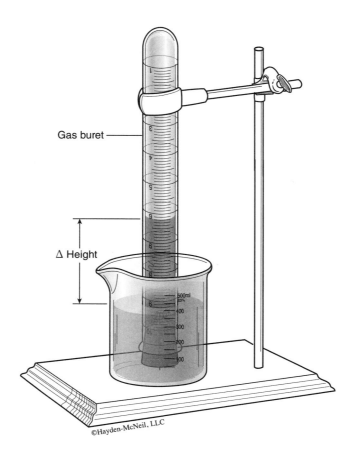

Gas buret

Δ Height

©Hayden-McNeil, LLC

Figure 10-2. Gas buret.

9. As the reaction takes place, the hydrogen gas rises and displaces acid solution out through the hole in the stopper into the beaker. If the metal sample should break loose from the copper wire, the hydrogen bubbles may make it buoyant enough to rise to the top of the liquid. If this occurs, gently tap the sides of the tube at the liquid surface so that the metal stays in the acid solution and does not stick to the walls of the tube.

    Once all evolution of hydrogen gas ceases, tap any hydrogen bubbles adhering to the walls of the tube or the copper wire so that they rise to the top. Allow the apparatus to cool to room temperature, and then make and record the following measurements:

    a. Record the final volume reading of hydrogen gas.

    b. Obtain the temperature of hydrogen gas by holding a thermometer against the outside wall of the gas tube. Record the value on the data sheet.

    c. Measure and record the temperature of the water in the beaker.

d. Obtain a ruler from your laboratory instructor and measure the difference in height between the water surface in the beaker and the water surface inside the gas tube (see Figure 10-2). Record the difference in water levels in mm.

e. Record the barometer reading and barometer temperature (provided by your instructor).

10. Carefully empty the contents of the gas tube down the sink, followed by lots of water. Repeat steps 4–9d of the procedure with two additional samples of the same metal.

11. Thoroughly clean the gas tube, and return the tube, ruler, thermometer and stopper to the laboratory instructor. Have your instructor sign your data sheet and lock your drawer before leaving.

IV. Calculations

The volume, temperature, and pressure of hydrogen gas must first be determined. The volume of hydrogen is simply the difference between the initial and final volume readings on the gas tube. The pressure of hydrogen must be corrected for the presence of water vapor mixed with the hydrogen, and for the difference from atmospheric pressure as evidenced in the different water levels in the gas tube and in the beaker.

In Figure 10-2, the pressure inside the tube is less than atmospheric pressure. To determine the actual pressure of the gases (hydrogen and water vapor) inside the tube, a correction for the difference in water levels must be made. The height difference, in mm H_2O can be equated to a pressure difference in mm Hg, using the relationship:

$$\text{mm Hg} = \text{mm } H_2O \text{ (density } H_2O/\text{density Hg)}$$

(where $\delta_{Hg} = 13.596$ g/mL and δ_{H_2O} can be found in the appendix)

The pressure of the gases can be calculated as follows:

$$P_{hydrogen} + P_{water\ vapor} = P_{barometric} - \Delta_{height} \text{ (mm Hg)}$$

The corrections for barometer readings at various temperatures, the density of water, and the vapor pressure of water are all listed in tables in the appendix.

Once the pressure, volume, and temperature of the hydrogen gas are known, the ideal gas law can be used to calculate the number of moles of hydrogen produced.

$$n = PV/RT; \text{ where } R = 62.358 \text{ L-torr/mol-K}$$

The stoichiometry of the reactions is used to determine the number of moles of metal reacted. The mass of the metal sample divided by the number of moles of metal reacted gives the gram-atomic weight of the metal.

$$\text{gram-atomic weight} = \text{mass of metal sample/moles of metal}$$

In completing the laboratory report, be sure to show the complete sample calculation where required. The calculation should include a formula or equation (if applicable), and all numbers should be complete with units.

The deviation is the difference between individual trials and the average value, and the average deviation is the average of the absolute values of the deviations. Since the identity of the metal used is known, it is also possible to calculate the error in your experimental results.

$$\% \text{ error} = \frac{[\text{experimental value} - \text{actual value}]}{\text{actual value}} \times 100\%$$

[Report Form]

_____

Name   Section #

_____

Instructor's Signature   Date

I. Data

Record data in ink, with units and the correct number of significant figures.

a. Metal used: _____

	Trial 1	Trial 2	Trial 3
b. Weight of beaker + sample	_____	_____	_____
c. Weight of empty beaker	_____	_____	_____
d. Initial reading of gas tube	_____	_____	_____
e. Final reading of gas tube	_____	_____	_____
f. Temperature of hydrogen gas	_____	_____	_____
g. Difference in water levels (mm H_2O)	_____	_____	_____
h. Temperature of water in beaker	_____	_____	_____
i. Density of water at temp (h)*	_____	_____	_____
j. Aqueous vapor pressure (mm Hg)* (use temperature in item f above)	_____	_____	_____

k. Barometer reading: _____ mm Hg (from instructor)

l. Barometer temperature _____ °C (from instructor)

m. Barometer scale correction*: _____ mm Hg

    * in appendix

II. Calculations

	Trial 1	Trial 2	Trial 3
1. Weight of sample	_____	_____	_____
2. Volume of gas collected	_____	_____	_____

3. Corrected barometric pressure: Show calculation.

_____ mm Hg

4. Mercury equivalent of difference in water levels—Show calculation for Trial 1.

Trial 1	Trial 2	Trial 3
_____	_____	_____
	millimeters of mercury	

5. Pressure of H_2—Show calculation for Trial 1.

Trial 1	Trial 2	Trial 3
_____	_____	_____
	millimeters of mercury	

6. Absolute temperature of H_2—Show calculation for Trial 1.

_____K _____K _____K

[Report Form continued]

Name _____   Section # _____

7. Moles of hydrogen produced—Use PV=nRT; Show calculation for Trial 1.
   [R = 62.358 1-torr/mol-K]

_____ _____ _____

moles of hydrogen

8. Moles of metal—Use item 7 above and the stoichiometry of the reaction.
   Show calculation for Trial 1.

_____ _____ _____

moles of metal (Mg or Zn)

9. Experimental gram-atomic weight of metal. Show calculation for Trial 1.

_____ _____ _____

grams/mole

10. Mean gram-atomic weight of _____metal: _____g/mol

11. Deviation of each trial from the mean. Show calculation for Trial 1.

_____ _____ _____

12. Average deviation. Show calculation.

average deviation= _____

13. Actual gram-atomic weight of _____ metal: _____ g/mol

14. % error. Show calculation.

% error= _____

[Report Form continued]

Name   Section #

III. Questions and Problems

1. Suppose you wanted to perform this experiment using aluminum metal. Assuming a volume of hydrogen of 65 mL, a final gas temperature of 25°C, and a gas pressure of approximately 720 torr, calculate the appropriate amount of aluminum, in grams, to be reacted. (Hint: Use the information about the hydrogen gas and work backwards. Be sure to include a balanced chemical equation for the reaction of aluminum with HCl to produce hydrogen gas.) Show your work.

answer: grams Al =_____

2. At STP, what volume of hydrogen will be produced by the reaction of .0379 grams of K with HCl? Show all your work and include a balanced chemical equation.

3. A metal strip containing a mixture (alloy) of magnesium and zinc was dissolved in HCl according to the procedure of this experiment. The sample has a mass of 0.1000 g, and produces 63.79 mL of hydrogen at STP. Calculate the mass of zinc and the mass of magnesium contained in the sample.

Experiment 11

Comparison of Antacid Tablet Effectiveness

I. Introduction

Many commercial products are sold for the relief of gastric hyperacidity. Such products are commonly called "antacids." In this experiment you will determine the relative effectiveness of several commercial preparations in neutralizing stomach acid, in terms of the amount of acid consumed per antacid tablet.

The human stomach contains cells in its walls that secrete hydrochloric acid (HCl) during the digestive process. The acid is needed during the digestive process to activate the stomach enzyme **pepsin**, which begins the digestion of proteins. A strong acid like HCl also often causes a change in the shapes of food molecules, which opens them to attack by enzymes found in the small intestine. The hydrochloric acid in the stomach is typically found at a concentration of 0.1 M (moles per liter). Occasionally, if a person overeats, or eats certain types of foods, the stomach may secrete *more* hydrochloric acid than is needed. This may result in the uncomfortable condition of "heartburn."

Commercial antacids come in a variety of formulas. Among those substances found in various formulations are: sodium hydrogen carbonate [$NaHCO_3$, sodium bicarbonate, "bicarb"], calcium carbonate [$CaCO_3$], magnesium hydroxide [$Mg(OH)_2$, milk of magnesia], and a mixture of magnesium hydroxide and aluminum hydroxide [$Al(OH)_3$, Maalox]. The reactions of these substances with HCl are below:

$$NaHCO_{3(s)} + HCl_{(aq)} \rightarrow NaCl_{(aq)} + H_2O_{(l)} + CO_{2(g)}$$

$$CaCO_{3(s)} + 2\,HCl_{(aq)} \rightarrow CaCl_{2(aq)} + H_2O_{(l)} + CO_{2(g)}$$

$$Mg(OH)_{2(s)} + 2\,HCl_{(aq)} \rightarrow MgCl_{2(aq)} + 2\,H_2O_{(l)}$$

$$Al(OH)_{3(s)} + 3\,HCl_{(aq)} \rightarrow AlCl_{3(aq)} + 3\,H_2O_{(l)}$$

Notice that the products of these reactions include an inert salt (e.g., NaCl) and water. Two of the antacid substances ($NaHCO_3$ and $CaCO_3$) also produce carbon dioxide gas, which may provide added relief to the heartburn (as a belch).

SAFETY PRECAUTIONS
- **Wear safety glasses at all times.**
- **Place the buret below eye level when filling with NaOH solution.**
- **Hydrochloric acid and sodium hydroxide solutions are corrosive to skin and eyes. Wash if spilled. Clean up any spills on the benchtop to prevent injury to other students.**

II. Equipment Needed

This experiment requires the following:

- 250 mL Erlenmeyer flask
- 50 mL and 10 mL graduated cylinders
- 50 mL buret with clamp and stand

III. Procedure

1. Obtain an antacid tablet. Record the brand name, active ingredient, and *amount* of active ingredient (from the label). Break the tablet into smaller pieces (being careful not to lose any of the tablet) and place into a 250 mL Erlenmeyer flask.

2. Obtain 50.0 mL of 0.500 M HCl (**Caution!**) and add to the tablet. If your tablet's active ingredient is carbonate or hydrogen carbonate, the tablet may fizz at this point as carbon dioxide is released. This concentration of HCl is 5 times more concentrated than stomach acid, but is chosen to speed up the dissolution of the tablet in the lab.

3. Allow the tablet to dissolve as much as possible. Antacid tablets usually contain fillers, binders, and flavorings that may not dissolve completely. Some antacids contain colored dyes that may impart a color to the solution at this point. Record any such color on the report page.

4. Add five drops of phenolphthalein indicator solution to the tablet/HCl mixture. If the tablet/HCl solution remains the same color, proceed directly to step 6. If the tablet/HCl solution changes color (from colorless to red for antacids which do not contain any colored dyes) when the phenolphthalein is added, continue on to step 5. If your tablet solution was already colored due to dyes in the tablet (step 3), the red color of the phenolphthalein will be modified by the colored dye already present. For example, if the solution was blue due to colored dyes in the tablet, then the appearance of the red phenolphthalein color would make the mixture appear purple. The thing to look for is a *change* in color when the phenolphthalein was added.

5. If the tablet/HCl mixture changed color when phenolphthalein was added, then not enough HCl had been added to react with the tablet's active ingredient. Add additional 0.500 M HCl, in 10 mL portions, until the color due to the phenolphthalein is gone. *Keep track of the total volume of HCl that has been added.*

6. Clean a 50 mL buret. Rinse the buret with three 5 mL portions of 0.500 M NaOH solution (**Caution!**). Discard the rinsings. Then fill the buret with 0.500 M NaOH (including the buret tip) and take a reading of the initial volume of NaOH in the buret. You need not start at exactly 0.00 mL.

7. Slowly begin adding NaOH from the buret to the flask containing the antacid tablet solution. As NaOH is added, it reacts with the portion of HCl that was not consumed by the tablet. As the NaOH solution enters the tablet solution, the red color of phenolphthalein may be visible as streaks. Swirl the flask; the red streaks should disappear as the solutions mix. Eventually it will take longer and longer for the red streaks to disappear. Finally, when the correct amount of NaOH has been added from the buret, one additional drop of NaOH will cause the tablet solution to take on a permanent pink color. If your tablet solution was already colored due to dyes in the tablet, the color at the endpoint of the reaction will be modified. Record the final volume level of NaOH solution in the buret. Estimate one place beyond the smallest divisions on the buret.

IV. Calculations

This experiment makes use of what is called a "back titration" method. It is difficult for technical reasons to analyze directly the active ingredient in an antacid tablet. Rather, a measured amount of 0.500 M HCl solution that is *more than that required to react with the tablet* was added. Then, the amount of excess HCl, beyond what is consumed by the antacid, is determined with 0.500 M NaOH solution. The *difference* between the amount of HCl initially taken and the remaining amount of HCl that is titrated with NaOH represents the amount of HCl that was consumed by the tablet.

Comparison Based on Price

Part of this experiment is to **compare** the effectiveness of the various antacids. On the second page of your report, you are asked to compare results for *your* analysis with the results *other students* obtained for different brands of antacid.

To do this, you will be completing part of your report *while still in the laboratory.* When you have finished your report as far as the section on "Mass of HCl consumed by tablet," please *write your results on the chalkboard at the front of the room* using this format:

Brand of Antacid _____ Mass of HCl consumed _____

Since you need to compare your results with the results obtained by other students, you should wait until at least **two** other brands of antacid have been reported on the chalkboard. That is two **additional brands** of antacid, not two students reporting on the same antacid brand.

114

You will need information about the cost and ingredients of the antacids being tested. Your instructor will give you the information so that you may fill in the following table and complete the calculations needed for your laboratory report.

avg.

.3906g ←

.583 g ←

.1533g ←

.384g ←

Brand Antacid	# Tablets	mg Active Ingredients	Cost
Rite Aid	150	500 Ca CO₃	$7.79
Maalox	90	1600 CaCO₃	$6.99
Rolaid	150	550 &110	$9.45
Philips	200	311 Mg(OH)₂	$10.99
Tums	150	500 CaCO₃	$9.99

12 Experiment

Molecular Shapes

I. Introduction

In this laboratory activity, you will be provided with a set of molecular models and be asked to construct and describe the shapes and properties of a variety of molecules and complex ions.

Prior to coming to class, you should work out the Lewis structures (electron dot diagrams) for each of the molecules and ions you will be asked to construct. If you have any questions concerning the dot diagrams, consult with your instructor before attempting to build the molecular model.

Once the model has been constructed, you will be asked to draw the model, provide bond angles, provide the molecular shape, determine whether the molecule or ion is polar or nonpolar and determine the hybridization of the central atom.

II. Procedure

Before coming to class, write the Lewis structures for each of the molecules or ions to be constructed. Although you should be familiar with the method for writing Lewis structures, the general procedure is outlined below.

A. Writing Lewis Structures
1. Determine the central atom. The central atom is usually the first element (other than hydrogen which is virtually **never** central) written in the formula.

   For example, CO_2, carbon, is central; HNO_3, nitrogen, is central. In the oxy acids, the hydrogen atoms are always attached to oxygen, and not the central atom.

2. Once the basic layout of the atoms has been determined, write in the valence electrons for the central atom, using one electron from the central atom to make a single bond with all the atoms it is bonded to.

3. Add valence electrons from the other atoms to the diagram, using one electron to complete all the single bonds and attach the atoms.

4. If the Lewis structure is for an ion, make sure the appropriate number of electrons is added (for anions) or removed (for cations) before proceeding.

5. Determine which atoms have an octet. (See exceptions to the octet rule below.)

6. Move electrons and/or make multiple bonds until the octet rule is met.

EXCEPTIONS TO THE OCTET RULE

a. Very small atoms, such as boron and beryllium, are not always capable of accommodating 8 electrons. Hydrogen can only accommodate a pair of electrons.

b. Molecules with an odd number of electrons will not obey the octet rule.

c. Elements in the 3rd period and higher can have expanded valence shells, with a maximum of 12 electrons.

B. Constructing Molecular Models

Examine the central atom of each Lewis structure, and add up the number of atoms attached to the central atom plus the number of lone pairs of electrons on the central atom.

For example, the Lewis diagram for water shows two hydrogen atoms and two lone pairs of electrons attached to the central O atom.

$$H \cdot\cdot \ddot{O} \cdot\cdot H$$

Since the total number of atoms plus lone pairs of electrons on the central atom equals four, the shape will be **based on** a tetrahedron (see the table on the next page). To construct the model, you must choose a central plastic piece which has four nubs at tetrahedral angles. However, the two corners of the tetrahedron occupied by the lone pair of electrons are invisible, so the **actual** molecular shape will be **bent or angular**, with a bond angle slightly less than 109.5°. The angle is less than that of a perfect tetrahedron because the repulsion between the two lone pairs forces the hydrogen atoms slightly closer together.

In structures with double or triple bonds, remember to count the number of atoms attached to the central atom, and not the number of bonds.

For example, in sulfur dioxide, the Lewis diagram is:

$$\left[\ddot{O} :: \overset{+1}{\ddot{S}} \cdot\cdot \ddot{O} : ^{-1} \right] \quad \longleftrightarrow \quad \left[^{-1} : \ddot{O} \cdot\cdot \overset{+1}{\ddot{S}} :: \ddot{O} \right]$$

The sulfur atom is attached to 2 atoms, and has one lone pair of electrons attached to it. The molecular shape is based on the sum of: 2 atoms + 1 lone pair = 3. To construct the model, you must choose a central plastic piece which has three nubs to accommodate three pairs of electrons. This piece would serve as the central atom for SO_2.

Once you have added up the # of atoms + lone pairs of electrons, you can predict the shape which the molecule is **based on** (this may not be the actual shape) using the outline below.

# of Atoms + Lone Pairs of e	Basis Shape	Bond Angles
2	linear	180°
3	trigonal planar	120°
4	tetrahedron	109.5°
5	trigonal bipyramid	120°, 90°
6	octahedron	90°

To determine the **actual** shape of the molecule, construct the appropriate basis shape using the models, and then remove corners for each lone pair on the central atom.

For sulfur dioxide, the basis shape is trigonal planar, but one corner of the triangle will be missing due to the lone pair of electrons on sulfur. The actual shape of the molecule will be bent, with an approximate bond angle of 120°.

Below is a list of the number of bonds and central plastic pieces you will need to construct all the molecules specified in the procedure. The pieces are in specially marked beakers and should be returned to their proper place when you are finished with them. The color of the pieces, except for the terminal atoms, is not important.

1. After your instructor's presentation, work on the Lewis structures for each molecule or ion in the activity. Students will be asked to go up to the blackboard and show the class how they arrived at the correct Lewis structure.

2. Once all the Lewis structures have been reviewed by the class, obtain the materials listed below and start constructing, on your own, each of the molecules or ions in the procedure. Start by choosing the proper central atom and then adding the atoms attached to it. Remember to remove any "corners" of the shape if the central atom contains lone pairs of electrons.

You will need the following materials:

*   6 chemical bonds
*   6 terminal atoms (one nub) of one color
*   2 terminal atoms (one nub) of another color
*   1 divalent atom (two nubs)
*   1 trivalent atom (three nubs)
*   1 tetravalent atom (four nubs)
*   1 pentavalent atom (five nubs)
*   1 hexavelent atom (six nubs)

3. Fill in the report sheet for each of the molecules or ions listed. Include the Lewis structure, the molecular shape, molecular drawing with bond angles, and the polarity of the molecule and the hybridization of the central atom.

4. Have your instructor review your report, and if all items are completed, turn in your report **before** leaving the laboratory. Place all the molecular model pieces in the appropriate beakers and **turn in your lab report before leaving**. Reports will not be accepted after you leave the laboratory.

[Report Form]

Name _____   Section # _____

Instructor's Signature _____   Date _____

Molecular Shapes

For each molecule and ion listed below, provide the Lewis structure, then construct the molecule or ion using the molecular model set. After construction, describe the shape of the molecule and draw it, labeling the bond angles, and state whether the molecule is polar or nonpolar.

1. CH_4

   a. Lewis structure

   b. Drawing of shape (label angles)

   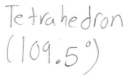

   Tetrahedron (109.5°)

   c. Name of shape ___Tetrahedron___

   d. Polar or nonpolar? ___Nonpolar___

2. NH_3

   a. Lewis structure

   b. Drawing of shape (label angles)

   c. Name of shape ___Tetrahedron___

   d. Polar or nonpolar? ___Polar___

3. H_2S

    a. Lewis structure   b. Drawing of shape (label angles)

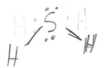

    c. Name of shape ___Tetrahedron_____

    d. Polar or nonpolar? _____

4. $CHCl_3$

    a. Lewis structure   b. Drawing of shape (label angles)

    c. Name of shape ___Tetrahedron_____

    d. Polar or nonpolar? _____

5. $SO_4{}^{2-}$

    a. Lewis structure   b. Drawing of shape (label angles)

    c. Name of shape ___Tetrahedron_____

    d. Polar or nonpolar? _____

[Report Form continued]

Name _____   Section # _____

6. CO_2

    a. Lewis structure   b. Drawing of shape (label angles)

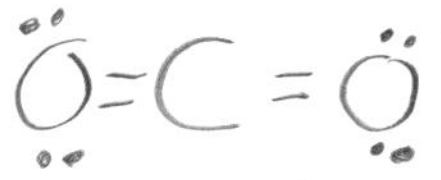

Ö=C=Ö

    c. Name of shape _____ Octahedron Linear _____

    d. Polar or nonpolar? _____

7. HCN

    a. Lewis structure   b. Drawing of shape (label angles)

H−C≡N

    c. Name of shape _____ Trigonal Planar Linear _____

    d. Polar or nonpolar? _____

8. SO_3

    a. Lewis structure   b. Drawing of shape (label angles)

    c. Name of shape _____ Trigonal Planar _____

    d. Polar or nonpolar? _____

9. NO_2^-

   a. Lewis structure

   b. Drawing of shape (label angles)

   $:\ddot{O}-\dot{N}=\ddot{O}$

   c. Name of shape ___Trigonal   Planar___

   d. Polar or nonpolar? _____

10. HNO_3

    a. Lewis structure

    b. Drawing of shape (label angles)

    $\ddot{O}=\ddot{N}-\ddot{O}-H$ with $\overset{\ddot{O}:}{|}$ above N

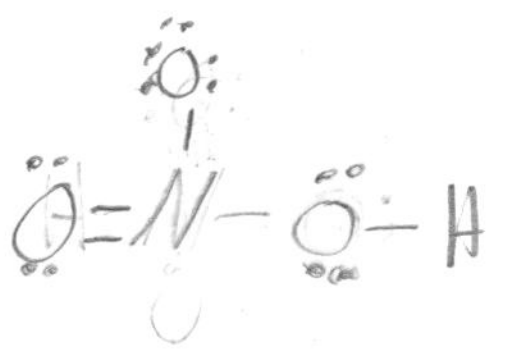

    c. Name of shape ___Tetrahedron___

    d. Polar or nonpolar? _____

11. $BeCl_2$

    a. Lewis structure

    b. Drawing of shape (label angles)

    $:\ddot{Cl}-Be-\ddot{Cl}:$

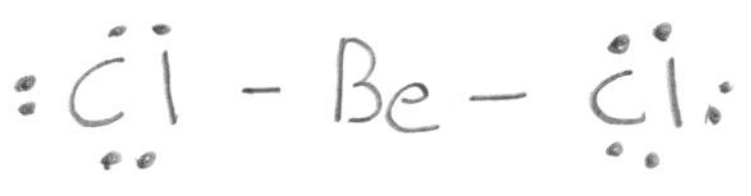

    c. Name of shape ___Linear___

    d. Polar or nonpolar? _____

[Report Form continued]

Name _____ Section # _____

12. BF_3

   a. Lewis structure   b. Drawing of shape (label angles)

   c. Name of shape _____

   d. Polar or nonpolar? _____

13. BrF_3

   a. Lewis structure   b. Drawing of shape (label angles)

   c. Name of shape __Trigonal Bipyramid_____

   d. Polar or nonpolar? _____

14. IF_2^-

   a. Lewis structure   b. Drawing of shape (label angles)

   c. Name of shape _____

   d. Polar or nonpolar? _____

15. SF_6

    a. Lewis structure   b. Drawing of shape (label angles)

    c. Name of shape _____

    d. Polar or nonpolar? _____

16. XeF_4

    a. Lewis structure   b. Drawing of shape (label angles)

    c. Name of shape _____

    d. Polar or nonpolar? _____

Experiment 13

Double Replacement Reactions

. I. Introduction

In this experiment, a variety of double replacement reactions will be studied. A double replacement reaction occurs when two soluble salts combine to form a product which is either a solid (formed as a precipitate), a gas, or a pure liquid such as water. An example of a double replacement reaction is:

$$2 \, KI_{(aq)} + Pb(NO_3)_{2(aq)} \rightarrow PbI_{2(s)} + 2 \, KNO_{3(aq)}$$

The above reaction occurs because lead(II) iodide is insoluble, and precipitates out of solution. By writing all aqueous reactants and products as individual ions, we can write an *ionic equation*.

$$2 \, K^+_{(aq)} + 2 \, I^-_{(aq)} + Pb^{2+}_{(aq)} + 2 \, NO_3^-_{(aq)} \rightarrow PbI_{2(s)} + 2 \, K^+_{(aq)} + 2 \, NO_3^-_{(aq)}$$

If all ions which appear on both sides of the arrow in exactly the same form are eliminated, the result is called a *net-ionic equation*. This equation shows only the ions which combine to form the precipitate. The potassium ion and nitrate ion don't participate in the formation of the precipitate, and they are called *spectator ions*.

$$2 \, I^-_{(aq)} + Pb^{2+}_{(aq)} \rightarrow PbI_{2(s)}$$

The formation of characteristic precipitates can be used to confirm the presence of certain ions. After examining many double replacement reactions and recording the formation and color of any precipitates formed, you will determine the identity of solutions of unknown salts.

II. Equipment Needed

This experiment requires the following:

- 24-well plate
- 96-well plate
- plastic dropper
- Kimwipes

III. Procedure

This experiment will be done in microscale. This means that only a few drops of solution will be used for each reaction. Special eyedroppers with very narrow openings will be used along with plastic plates which contain small indentations, called wells. The reactions will be carried out in these wells, rather than in test tubes or beakers.

1. Obtain one 24-well plate, one 96-well plate, and a plastic dropper from your equipment drawer. Rinse all items with tap water, then a small amount of distilled water, and dry the plates by shaking the plate over the sink to empty the wells, and then by using Kimwipes.

2. Using the 24-well plate, obtain several wells full of distilled water (for cleaning the dropper during the experiment), and half a well each of the following solutions. Be sure to record the locations of each solution and its color on the data sheet. The wells are labeled A1–6, B1–6, etc., as illustrated below.

The solutions to be used are:

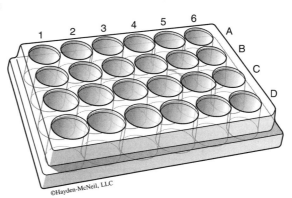

a. 0.1 M $BaCl_2$
b. 0.1 M $Pb(NO_3)_2$
c. 0.1 M $AgNO_3$
d. 0.1 M $NaOH$
e. 0.1 M Na_2CO_3
f. 0.1 M K_2CrO_4
g. 0.1 M $NiSO_4$

©Hayden-McNeil, LLC

Note: Clear and colorless are two different observations. Colored solutions can also be clear, just as the sky can be described as being clear and blue.

3. Using the 96-well plate, set up a grid for the reactions as illustrated on the next page. Set up the plate so that is has eight vertical columns, and twelve horizontal rows, with the corner notches in the upper left and right corners of the plate. Start by taking solution a, $BaCl_2$, and placing two drops in each of 7 wells in a vertical column (wells A12–6). Empty the dropper into the appropriate storage well of the 24-well plate, clean the dropper with distilled water, and then place drops of solution b, $Pb(NO_3)_2$, in the wells of the next vertical column

(wells B12–6). Repeat, rinsing the dropper between solutions, until the first seven vertical columns of the plate contain the seven solutions.

4. After rinsing the dropper, place two drops of solution a, $BaCl_2$, in each well in the first horizontal row (wells A12–G12). Carefully observe each well as you add the second solution, and note any cloudiness or changes in color. Record your observations on the data sheet. You can gently mix the contents of the wells by slowly moving the plate in a circular motion while keeping it on the benchtop. It may be easier to see the formation of solids by placing the plate on a sheet of paper or by holding it up to the light and viewing it from underneath.

5. Repeat step 4 using solution b, $Pb(NO_3)_2$, and place two drops in the second horizontal row (wells A11–G11). Repeat with the remaining solutions until the reaction grid, as illustrated below, is complete. Record all observations on the data sheet. If you are unsure if a precipitate has formed, repeat the reaction in a well on the edge of the plate and view the reaction mixture from the side. You should be able to see cloudiness or solid settling in the bottom of the well if a reaction has occurred.

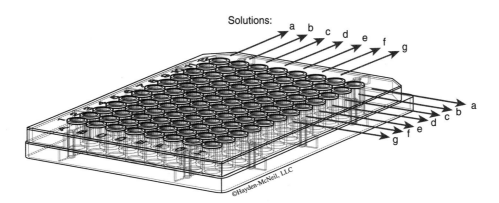

6. Obtain a half well of two unknown solutions, using your 24-well plate. Record the code number, well location, and note the color of each unknown. Conduct reactions between each unknown and the seven known solutions (a–g) until you can identify each of the unknowns.

    Each unknown will contain only one cation and one anion from the following group: Ba^{2+}, Pb^{2+}, Ag^+, Ni^{2+}, Cl^-, OH^-, SO_4^{2-}, CO_3^{2-} and CrO_4^{2-}.

7. Several additional solutions will be available. Consult the solubility table and, using these additional solutions and the original seven solutions (a–g), choose three new reactions which should produce a precipitate. Write the formula of the insoluble product you think will form on the data sheet along with the two solutions which will be mixed to form that precipitate. Mix two drops of each solution in a well in the 96-well plate, and record your observations. Did a precipitate form? What is its color? Record your observations on the data sheet.

8. Thoroughly clean both plates and the dropper. Make sure your instructor signs your data sheet and locks your drawer before leaving the laboratory.

Solubilities

	Br⁻	CO₃²⁻	Cl⁻	CrO₄²⁻	OH⁻	I⁻	NO₃⁻	PO₄³⁻	SO₄²⁻	S²⁻
Ba^{2+}	S	ss	S	I	ss	S	S	S	I	d
Ca^{2+}	S	ss	S	S	ss	S	S	ss	ss	ss
Cu^{2+}	S	I	S	I	I	I	S	I	S	I
Fe^{3+}	S	ss	S	I	I	S	S	I	S	d
Pb^{2+}	I	I	ss	I	ss	I	S	I	ss	I
Ni^{2+}	S	ss	S	S	ss	S	S	I	S	I
K^+	S	S	S	S	S	S	S	S	S	S
Ag^+	I	I	I	ss	d	I	S	I	ss	I
Na^+	S	S	S	S	S	S	S	S	S	S

I = Insoluble; **S** = Soluble; **ss** = Slightly soluble; **d** = Decomposes

IV. Laboratory Reports

You will be required to write "regular" and net-ionic equations for all double replacement reactions you performed. The easiest way to accomplish this is to proceed from left to right on the 96-well plate and assume a double replacement reaction has occurred wherever a well appears to be cloudy or contain a solid. Consult the solubility table and determine which of the possible products of the double replacement reaction is insoluble or slightly soluble.

For example, the well containing $BaCl_2$ and $Pb(NO_3)_2$ may appear cloudy. Possible products of a double replacement reaction are barium nitrate, $Ba(NO_3)_2$, and lead(II) chloride. $PbCl_2$. The solubility table shows that barium nitrate is soluble, and that lead chloride is slightly soluble (ss). The reaction for the double replacement reaction which caused the cloudiness is:

$$BaCl_{2(aq)} + Pb(NO_3)_{2(aq)} \rightarrow Ba(NO_3)_{2(aq)} + PbCl_{2(s)} \text{ a white precipitate}$$

Note that all solutions and soluble salts are written as aqueous, and the slightly soluble (or insoluble) salt is noted with an (s) for solid. The net-ionic equation is simply the reaction between the two ions which react to form the insoluble product. In this example the net-ionic equation is:

$$Pb^{2+}_{(aq)} + 2\,Cl^-_{(aq)} \rightarrow PbCl_{2(s)}$$

In addition to writing equations, you are required to identify two unknown salts. **133**
You must identify both the cation and the anion based on your observations when
reacting the unknown with the seven solutions previously listed. Each unknown will
contain only one cation and one anion from the following group:

$$Ba^{2+}, Pb^{2+}, Ag^+, Ni^{2+}, Cl^-, OH^-, SO_4{}^{2-}, CO_3{}^{2-} \text{ and } CrO_4{}^{2-}$$

Use your observations (including the color of the unknown solutions) and the solubility table to aid you in identifying the salt solution.

134

[Report Form]

Henry von kelsch   84.123

Name   Section #

_____

Instructor's Signature   Date

I. Data

For each solution in the 24-well plate, note the location and the color.

a. $BaCl_2$:   well # A1   color Colorless

b. $Pb(NO_3)_2$:   well # A2   color Colorless

c. $AgNO_3$:   well # A3   color Colorless

d. NaOH: well # A4   color Colorless

e. Na_2CO_3:   well # A5   color Colorless

f. K_2CrO_4:   well # A6   color Yellow

g. $NiSO_4$:   well # A7   color Green

II. Observations

96-well plate: Fill in any observations in the appropriate place in the grid.

	$BaCl_2$	$Pb(NO_3)_2$	$AgNO_3$	NaOH	Na_2CO_3	K_2CrO_4	$NiSO_4$
$BaCl_2$	N	N	White	white	white	Yellow	white
$Pb(NO_3)_2$	N	N	N	white	white	Yellow	white
$AgNO_3$	white	N	N	Brown	white	Red	N
NaOH	white	white	Brown	N	N	N	White
Na_2CO_3	white	white	White	N	N	N	white
K_2CrO_4	Yellow	Yellow	Red	NO	N	N	N
$NiSO_4$	White	white	N	white	white	N	N
Unk# 615	N	N	white	N	N	N	N
Unk# 416	White	N	N	Brown	white	Red	N

Step 7 of the procedure: Reactions of "Extra" Solutions. Perform 3 new reactions which should form an insoluble product.

Precipitate to Be Formed	Solutions to Be Mixed	Observations
1. $AgCl^-$	$CaCl_2$ & $AgNO_3$	White/Cloudy
2. None	$CaCl_2$ & $BaCl_2$	Colorless/clear
3. None	$CaCl_2$ & $Pb(NO_3)_2$	Colorless/clear

III. Chemical Equations

Using your observations of cloudiness or precipitation and the solubilities of possible reaction products, write a balanced chemical equation for all reactions which produced an <u>insoluble</u> or <u>slightly soluble product</u>. Write only the reactions which you observed to occur (i.e., form a solid). Write both the "<u>regular</u>" equation and the <u>net-ionic equation.</u> Be sure to note the color of any precipitates formed. Although results will vary. there should be between 10 and 15 different reactions which produced a precipitate. If you look at the way the grid was set up, you will realize that each reaction was performed twice. You need only write the equation once.

1. Reactions of barium chloride (first row left to right).

$$BaCl_2 + 2AgNO_3 \rightarrow Ba(NO_3)_2 + 2AgCl$$
$$BaCl_2 + 2NaOH \rightarrow Ba(OH)_2 + 2NaCl$$
$$BaCl_2 + Na_2CO_3 \rightarrow BaCO_3 + 2NaCl$$
$$BaCl_2 + K_2CrO_4 \rightarrow 2KCl + BaCrO_4$$
$$BaCl_2 + NiSO_4 \rightarrow BaSO_4 + NiCl$$

2. Reactions of lead(II) nitrate (second row left to right, other than the ones listed above).

$$Pb(NO_3)_2 + 2NaOH \rightarrow Pb(OH)_2 + 2Na(NO_3)$$
$$Pb(NO_3)_2 + Na_2CO_3 \rightarrow PbCO_3 + 2NaNO_3$$

[Report Form continued]

Name   Section #

3. Reactions of silver nitrate (third row left to right, other than the ones listed previously).

4. Reactions of sodium hydroxide (fourth row, other than the ones listed previously).

5. Reactions of sodium carbonate (fifth row, other than the ones listed previously).

6. Reactions of potassium chromate (sixth row, other than the ones listed previously).

7. Reactions of nickel(II) sulfate (seventh row, other than the ones listed previously).

IV. Unknowns
Identify both unknowns, and explain your reasoning.

a. unknown _____ contains _____ because

b. unknown _____ contains _____ because

V. Reactions of "Extra" Solutions (Step 7 of the procedure).
Write the balanced net-ionic equations for the three new reactions you performed. Include the color of the precipitate formed.

1.

2.

3.

[Report Form continued]

Name   Section #

VI. Questions

1. Using the solubility table, complete and balance the following possible double replacement reactions. Use the notation N.R. for no reaction.

   a. $Na_3PO_{4(aq)} + NiSO_{4(aq)} \rightarrow$

   b. $KNO_{3(aq)} + Pb(NO_3)_{2(aq)} \rightarrow$

   c. $Na_3PO_{4(aq)} + BaCl_{2(aq)} \rightarrow$

   d. $FeI_{3(aq)} + Cu(NO_3)_{2(aq)} \rightarrow$

140

Experiment 14

Spectrophotometric Determination of Dyes

I. Introduction

Compounds which are colored absorb electromagnetic radiation in the visible region. The wavelength (or color) of the radiation absorbed depends on the chemical nature of the compound. In this experiment, the absorption of radiation by dyes will be examined using an instrument called a *spectrophotometer*. A spectrophotometer can measure the intensity of electromagnetic radiation at various wavelengths. In the visible range, the wavelength at which a given compound absorbs the maximum amount of radiation is directly related to the color of the compound. For example, compounds which appear blue in color absorb light with wavelengths from 580–600 nanometers (nm, equal to 10^{-9} meters), and compounds which appear red in color absorb light with wavelengths of approximately 490 nm. Most compounds have a specific wavelength where they absorb a maximum amount of radiation. This wavelength is called λ_{max}, where λ (lambda) is the symbol for wavelength, and λ_{max} stands for maximum absorbance of radiation.

For most colored compounds, the extent to which light at λ_{max} is absorbed is directly related to how many molecules of the compound are present. That is, samples which contain high concentrations of a colored compound will absorb more radiation at λ_{max} than dilute samples of the same compound. This relationship, called the Beer–Lambert law, has been used to determine the concentrations of very dilute samples of compounds.

In order to use the Beer–Lambert relationship between absorbance of radiation and concentration, some terms must be defined. The liquid sample is placed in a special test tube or cell, and exposed to light of the appropriate wavelength. The intensity of the radiation entering the cell is compared to the intensity of the radiation leaving the cell. The amount of radiation absorbed by the sample will depend on the nature of the substance, the concentration of the sample, and the length of the path of light as it travels through the cell.

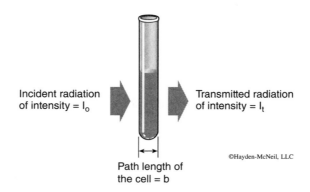

Incident radiation
of intensity = I_o

Transmitted radiation
of intensity = I_t

©Hayden-McNeil, LLC

Path length of
the cell = b

The absorbance of the sample, A, is related to the path length, concentration and nature of the compound by the following equation.

$$A = \varepsilon bc = \left(\frac{I_o}{I_t} \right)$$

Where   A = absorbance, and can be obtained from the spectrophotometer

ε = molar absorbtivity or molar extinction coefficient, and depends on the nature of the compound

c = molarity of the absorbing compound

The fraction I_t/I_o is defined as the transmittance. The percent transmittance (%T) is $I_t/I_o \times 100\%$, and can be read directly from the scale on the spectrophotometer. Since the %T scale is linear and the absorbance scale is logarithmic, it is easier to read % transmittance and convert it to absorbance as follows.

$$A = \varepsilon bc = \log \left(\frac{100}{\%T} \right) = 2 - \log \%T$$

If the same cell is used for all measurements, then b, the path length, is constant. Likewise, ε, the extinction coefficient, is constant for a given compound. Thus, a graph of absorbance versus concentration (in moles/liter or comparable units) should produce a straight line. Such a graph, illustrated in Figure 14-1, is called a Beer's law plot, and can be obtained by preparing several solutions of known concentration and measuring absorbance (or measuring %T and calculating the absorbance). The slope of the line equals εb, or the extinction coefficient times the path length.

The Beer's Law plot can be used to determine the concentration of a solution of the compound. Once the graph has been created using solutions of known concentration, the absorbance of a solution of unknown concentration can be measured using a spectrophotometer. The absorbance can then be correlated to concentration using the graph.

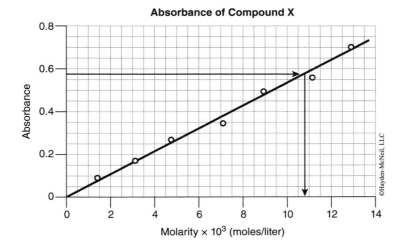

Figure 14-1. Graph of absorbance versus molarity for compound X.

Using the graph for compound X, a solution of unknown concentration had an absorbance of 0.58. The arrow is drawn from the measured absorbance to the line on the graph and then down to the concentration of the solution. The solution has a concentration of approximately 10.8×10^{-3} moles/liter.

In this experiment, you will determine the concentration of a solution after creating a Beer's law plot. The compound to be studied is a colored dye.

II. Equipment Needed

This experiment requires the following:

- 250 mL volumetric flask (from instructor's desk)
- 50 mL buret (from instructor's desk)
- 100 mL beaker
- funnel
- 5 medium-sized test tubes
- test tube rack
- Kimwipes
- wash bottle
- 250 mL waste beaker
- 100 mL beaker

III. Procedure

1. A stock solution of known concentration will be available in each laboratory. Record the name of the compound, the concentration of the stock solution and the wavelength to be used on the data sheet. Using a clean dry 100 mL beaker, obtain 75 mL of the stock solution and cover it with a watch glass.

2. Clean a 50 mL buret with soap solution, then rinse with tap water. Line the buret three times with 5 mL portions of distilled water, making sure to rinse the tip of the buret each time. Finally, line the buret three times with 5 mL portions of the stock solution, making sure some of the solution runs through the tip each time.

3. Using a funnel, fill the buret with stock solution. Remove the funnel, and run some of the solution through the tip to expel any air bubbles. Read at the bottom of the meniscus and record the buret reading to the nearest 0.01 mL. You do not need to start at the zero line.

4. You will be preparing several solutions of varying concentrations using the buret to measure the volume of stock solution and a 250 mL volumetric flask to dilute the stock solution to a known volume. The volumetric flask should be cleaned and rinsed with tap water and then distilled water. It does not need to be dry. Deliver approximately 2 mL of stock solution into the volumetric flask. Record the buret reading after the addition to the nearest 0.01 mL.

5. Using a large beaker containing distilled water, fill the volumetric flask approximately halfway and swirl the flask to mix the contents. After mixing, add water until the level reaches the base of the neck of the flask. Fill a clean eyedropper with distilled water and slowly add water until the bottom of the water line is even with the fill line on the flask.

   If you have a plastic flask, the water line will appear flat, and should be just at the line on the neck of the flask. If your volumetric flask is made of glass, the bottom of the curved surface of the water (called the meniscus) should be sitting on the line on the neck of the flask.

©Hayden-McNeil, LLC

Figure 14-2. For a glass flask, fill with distilled water until the bottom of the meniscus is on the fill line.

6. Cap the volumetric flask and invert it several times to thoroughly mix the contents. Label a clean test tube "solution #1" and rinse the test tube several times with your solution. Transfer at least 10 mL of the solution to the test tube. Discard the remaining solution in the flask down the sink and rinse the flask with distilled water.

7. Take a buret reading (to the nearest 0.01 mL) and record it on the data sheet. Deliver a volume of approximately 5 mL of stock dye solution to the volumetric flask. Record the buret reading after addition, and fill the flask and mix the contents as in steps 5 and 6. After rinsing a second test tube with this solution, transfer at least 10 mL of the solution to the test tube and label it #2. Discard the rest of the solution down the sink. Rinse the volumetric flask with distilled water.

8. Repeat the previous steps, making three more solutions containing approximately 10 mL, 15 mL, and 20 mL of stock solution diluted to a volume of 250 mL. Be sure to record your initial and final buret readings to the nearest 0.01 mL. Place portions of each solution in test tubes labeled solution #3, #4, and #5.

9. Bring the test tube rack containing your five solutions, Kimwipes, a wash bottle, a waste beaker, and your lab manual and pen to the Spectronic 20 spectrophotometer. Record the identification number of the Spectronic 20 you use on the data sheet.

10. Following the instructions in the appendix (also located near the spectrophotometer), standardize the instrument for 0% and 100% transmittance. The solvent cell should be filled with distilled water, and the wavelength set to λ_{max}.

Line up the white etch mark with the line on the cell holder.

©Hayden-McNeil, LLC

Figure 14-3. Line up the white etch mark with the line on the cell holder.

When inserting the special cells (called cuvettes) into the sample holder, make sure the etching on the cell lines up with the mark on the holder. The cell should be filled only halfway. Be sure to wipe the outside with a Kimwipe and to handle the cell on the top half only.

11. Starting with the most dilute solution, rinse the Spectronic 20 solution cell with a small portion of solution #1. Fill the cell halfway with the solution, wipe the outside of the cell with a Kimwipe, and insert it in the cell holder. Read and record the % transmittance (to the nearest 0.1%T) of the solution on the data sheet. When making measurements, stand directly in front of the meter to avoid parallax. Use the mirror on the scale to be sure you are standing in the proper position. The reflection of the needle should be obscured by the needle when you're in the correct position.

12. Discard the contents of the cell in the waste beaker, and repeat the rinsing, filling, and wiping of the cell with solution #2. Following the instructions in the appendix, standardize the instrument for 0% and 100% transmittance. The solvent cell should be filled with distilled water, and the wavelength set to λ_{max}. Place the cell with solution #2 in the spectrophotometer, and read and record the % transmittance of the solution. Repeat this step with solutions #3–5, making sure to check the 0 and 100%T settings before making measurements.

13. Obtain a solution of the dye of unknown concentration from your instructor. Record the code number on your data sheet. After making sure that the **same Spectronic 20** you used for steps 11 and 12 has been standardized for 0 and 100% transmittance, measure the % transmittance of your unknown after following the rinsing procedure for the cell as outlined previously. Record the % transmittance on the data sheet. Measure the %T of your unknown two more times, making sure to restandardize the spectrophotometer at 0 and 100%T between measurements. Record the values for %T on the data sheet.

14. Rinse the solution cell with distilled water and place it in the rack located near the spectrophotometer. Discard the contents of the waste beaker in the sink. Return the volumetric flask and buret, and have your instructor sign your report form and lock your equipment drawer before leaving.

IV. Calculations

In order to determine the concentration of the unknown solution, you must prepare a Beer's law plot as described in the introduction of this experiment. The graph should be on mm × mm paper, with absorbance on the y-axis and concentration on the x-axis. Since measurements of % transmittance were made, you must first calculate the absorbance from the % transmittance using the equation in the introduction. When taking the logarithm of a number, the resulting log should have as many places after the decimal as significant figures in the original number. For example, a sample with a % transmittance of 26.3 (3 significant figures) has an absorbance of:

$$Abs = 2 - \log 26.3 = 2 - 1.420 = 0.580 \text{ (3 places after the decimal)}$$

The concentration units will not be moles/liter, as these dyes are so intensely colored that solutions which are as dilute as 0.001 M will give 0% transmittance readings on the Spectronic 20. Instead, for very dilute solutions, the unit "parts per million" (ppm) is used. Parts per million is the same as micrograms per milliliter. Thus a solution which is 100 ppm contains 100 micrograms (a microgram is 10^{-6} grams) of the solute per milliliter of solution, or 0.0001 grams per mL. Although this is very dilute, the concentrations of many atmospheric pollutants are measured in ppm since very dilute solutions can produce vast environmental damage.

In preparing your Beer's law plot, calculate the concentration of each of the solutions (#1–5) which you prepared as follows:

$$\text{concentration of solution} = \frac{(\text{concentration}_{stock})(V_{stock})}{\text{final volume of solution}}$$

For example, if the stock solution was 100 ppm, and 2.15 mL was diluted to a final volume of 250 mL, the concentration of the resulting solution is:

$$\frac{(\text{concentration}_{stock})(V_{stock})}{\text{final volume of solution}} = \frac{(100 \text{ ppm})(2.15 \text{ mL})}{250.00 \text{ mL}} = 0.860 \text{ ppm}$$

After calculating the absorbance and concentration of each solution, prepare the graph according to the instructions in the appendix. Make sure the scale is such that most of the page is used. The data should provide a straight line. Sometimes the data for the more dilute solutions is linear, with some curvature for the more concentrated solutions. Use a "see-through" ruler for drawing the best line through the linear portion of the data. If it curves, use a French curve or a "flexicurve" to represent the data.

Use the graph to find the concentration (in ppm) of the unknown solution as explained in the introduction to this experiment. Average your three values of %T, and use the average value to calculate the absorbance of your unknown. Locate the absorbance of your unknown on the graph, go horizontally across the graph until the line is reached, and then go down to read the concentration of the unknown. Draw in the arrows for your unknown on the graph as is done in the introduction section of this experiment. Include your graph, properly labeled, titled, etc., along with your laboratory report.

148

[Report Form]

Name _____   Section # _____

Instructor's Signature _____   Date _____

I. Data

Record data in ink, with units.

a. Name of compound _____

b. Color of compound _____

c. λ_{max} of compound _____

d. Concentration of stock solution _____

e.

Buret readings and volume:	Initial	Final	Volume
solution #1	_____	_____	_____
solution #2	_____	_____	_____
solution #3	_____	_____	_____
solution #4	_____	_____	_____
solution #5	_____	_____	_____

f. Spectroscopy data:

   1. Identification # on Spectronic 20: _____

   2. Percent transmittance of solutions #1–5

      solution #1: _____

      solution #2: _____

      solution #3: _____

      solution #4: _____

      solution #5: _____

   3. Data for unknown solution:

      a. Unknown # _____

      b. % transmittance: _____   _____   _____

      Trial 1   Trial 2   Trial 3

II. Calculations

Show a sample calculation, complete with equations, units, and the correct number of significant figures for solution #1.

a. Absorbance (calculated from % transmittance). Show a sample calculation for solution #1.

Results: _____   _____   _____   _____   _____

Solution #   1   2   3   4   5

b. Concentration of solutions #1–5: Show a sample calculation for solution #1.

Results: _____   _____   _____   _____   _____

Solution #   1   2   3   4   5

c. Average % Transmittance of Unknown: _____

d. Absorbance of Unknown: show calculation using average %T.

[Report Form continued]

Name _____ Section # _____

III. Results

a. Concentration of unknown # _____ is _____ (obtained from the graph)

b. Attach your graph and indicate on the Beer's law plot how you determined the concentration of your unknown.

IV. Questions

1. The cells used in the Spectronic 20 are precision made with a path length of 1.16 cm. Since Absorbance = εbc, the slope of your graph should equal ε, the extinction coefficient, times the path length b. Determine the slope of the line on your Beer's law plot, and use it to calculate the extinction coefficient of the dye. Indicate the points used to calculate the slope on your graph, and show all calculations below.

152

15 Experiment

Determination of Fe(II)—A Redox Titration

I. Introduction

In this experiment, the amount of ferrous ion (Fe^{2+}) in an unknown will be determined by the reaction with a standardized solution of potassium permanganate ($KMnO_4$). These reactants undergo the following oxidation–reduction half-reactions:

$$MnO_4^-{}_{(aq)} + 8\ H_3O^+{}_{(aq)} + 5\ e^- \leftrightarrow Mn^{2+}{}_{(aq)} + 12\ H_2O_{(l)}$$

$$Fe^{2+}{}_{(aq)} \leftrightarrow Fe^{3+}{}_{(aq)} + e^-$$

This titration must be carried out in strongly acidic solutions to prevent competing reactions from occurring. There are some advantages and disadvantages to using permanganate ion as the titrant. The main advantage is that it cannot only serve as the oxidizing agent, but also as the indicator. Permanganate ion had a very deep purple color, while the product, Mn^{2+}, is colorless at low concentrations. Thus, during the titration as the purple permanganate solution is added to the iron(II) solution, the purple color disappears. Once all of the iron(II) has reacted and a slight excess of permanganate has been added, the solution takes on a slight pink color. Another advantage of using permanganate ion is that its disposal does not cause the major environmental impact of many other oxidizing agents.

The major disadvantage of using permanganate ion is that solutions of $KMnO_4$ are not very stable. Permanganate ion can react with dust and other organic matter, so all solutions must be *standardized* so that the exact concentration of the permanganate ion can be determined. *Standardization* is the process by which one determines the concentration of a solution by reacting it with a known amount of another reagent. In this experiment, you will be provided with a solution of permanganate ion which is approximately 0.02 M. During the first week of this experiment, you will standardize the solution (determine its exact concentration) by reacting it with a known amount of iron(II) ion obtained from weighed samples of ferrous ammonium sulfate. Once the exact concentration of the $KMnO_4$ solution is known, the permanganate solution will be reacted with samples containing an unknown amount of iron(II), and the %Fe of the unknown will be determined. Analysis of the unknown takes place during the second week of the experiment.

II. Equipment Needed

This experiment requires the following:

- glass stirring rod
- funnel
- buret (from instructor)
- small beaker for weighing
- 2 Erlenmeyer flasks
- 10 mL graduated cylinder
- wash bottle
- unknown sample (from instructor)

III. Procedure

A. Week 1: Standardization of $KMnO_4$ Solution

1. Clean your 1 pint/500 mL plastic storage bottle, and then fill it about 80% full with the $KMnO_4$ solution that has been provided. Your bottle need not be dry. Label the bottle with your name.

   You will use this solution for both parts of the experiment.

   > *The bottle cannot be refilled* once you place the solution in it, because water in your bottle will have diluted the solution. Each student's solution will be unique, although they will have concentrations near 0.02 M. This experiment requires the concentration to be known precisely to 4 significant figures.

2. Clean a buret with 5 mL of soap solution and a buret brush. Rinse the buret with small portions of tap water until there is no evidence of soap. Then rinse with three 5 mL portions of distilled water by "lining" the buret. (Your instructor will demonstrate this technique.) Don't forget to let some water flow through the tip of the buret.

3. Place approximately 4 grams of $Fe(NH_4)_2(SO_4)_2 \cdot 6\,H_2O$ in a small clean dry beaker and obtain the mass of the sample and beaker using the electronic analytical balance. Record the mass (to the 4th decimal place) on the data sheet.

4. Transfer approximately 1.0 grams of $Fe(NH_4)_2(SO_4)_2 \cdot 6\,H_2O$ from the beaker to a clean (need not be dry) Erlenmeyer flask. Make sure all of the compound is transferred to the flask. If you spill any, rinse the flask and start again. (Remember to weigh the beaker and ferrous ammonium sulfate again before transferring.)

5. After quantitatively transferring the sample, weigh the beaker and remaining compound and record the mass. The difference is the mass of ferrous ammonium sulfate transferred. The mass need not be exactly 1.0 grams, but it must be known to the nearest 0.0001 gram. **Weigh only one sample, and proceed to the next step.**

6. Add 25 mL of distilled water to the sample in the Erlenmeyer flask and stir to dissolve. Mix the contents until the sample is dissolved. If you use a stirring rod, rinse the rod (using a wash bottle) into the flask before removing the rod. Then, using a graduated cylinder, slowly add 10 mL of 3 M H_2SO_4 solution, and mix the contents of the flask thoroughly. **CAUTION:** Sulfuric acid is caustic. Rinse all spills with sodium bicarbonate solution and then water. Report all spills to your instructor.

7. Rinse the buret with three 5 mL portions of your $KMnO_4$ solution by "lining" the buret. Then fill the buret with $KMnO_4$ solution using a funnel. Be sure to let some of the solution flow through the tip of the buret.

8. Remove the funnel from the buret and record the initial buret reading estimated to the nearest 0.01 mL. The reading need not be at the zero line. Since permanganate ion is so deeply colored, you may not be able to see the meniscus. You may record the level at the edge, rather than the meniscus, as long as you are consistent and make all readings in the same way. Be sure to read down, rather than up, as illustrated on the next page.

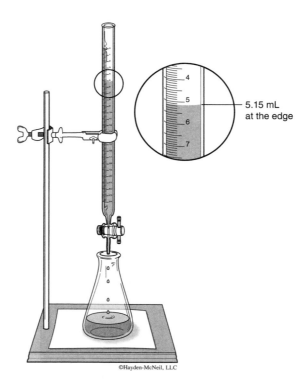

5.15 mL
at the edge

©Hayden-McNeil, LLC

9. Place the Erlenmeyer flask containing the sample under the buret, and lower the buret until the tip is inside the mouth of the flask. Titrate by adding permanganate solution to the flask. Add the first 5 mL of permanganate solution slowly so as to prevent the formation of insoluble MnO_2. Swirl the flask throughout the titration to mix the reactants. Periodically wash the inner walls of the flask with water using a wash bottle to make sure that the splashed sample or titrant are mixed.

    Add $KMnO_4$ until a faint pink color which lasts at least 15 seconds with stirring is observed in the flask. Record the buret reading to the nearest 0.01 mL in the same way as was done for the initial reading.

10. Repeat steps 4–6, refill the buret, and titrate as in step 9 until three trials have been performed. Make sure to record initial and final masses and buret readings. NOTE: You can estimate the volume of $KMnO_4$ which will be needed for each trial as follows:

$$\text{Estimated } V_{KMnO_4} = \frac{V_{KMnO_4} \text{ trial 1}}{\text{mass of sample 1}} \times \text{mass of new sample}$$

    Perform this calculation so that you can quickly add enough $KMnO_4$ to get near the endpoint. Then titrate slowly to get accurate results. **Do not use more than half of your $KMnO_4$ during standardization, or you will be unable to analyze the unknown next week, and will receive no credit for the experiment.**

11. Cap the storage bottle tightly. Calculate the molarity of the $KMnO_4$ solution for each titration. The first three non-zero digits in your molarities should be the same. If you know a sample was over-titrated, you may discard it, but be sure to indicate this on your report sheet. If you do not have at least three values of molarity which agree in the first three significant figures, perform additional trials.

12. After performing all the calculations required for the report, label your storage bottle with the average molarity, and also record it on the data sheet for week 2. Place the $KMnO_4$ solution in your locker standing up, not on its side. Return the buret, and make sure your instructor locks your locker.

B. Week 2: Analysis of Unknown Iron(II) Sample

1. Obtain a vial of unknown from your instructor and record the code number on your data sheet. Weigh the vial with contents on an analytical balance and record the mass on the data sheet.

2. Quantitatively transfer a sample weighing from 1.2–1.5 grams to a clean (need not be dry) Erlenmeyer flask and reweigh the vial and remaining unknown. Record the mass of the vial plus remaining contents on the data sheet. The difference in mass is the weight of sample transferred. **Weigh out only one sample of the unknown initially**, as you may need to adjust the sample size depending upon the iron content.

3. Treat the sample according to step 6 in Part A, and titrate as was done previously (steps 7–9, Part A). Make sure to record your initial and final buret reading to the nearest 0.01 mL.

4. If the volume of $KMnO_4$ needed for reaction is between 25–35 mL, perform two more trials using a similar (though not necessarily identical) mass of unknown. If the volume of titrant falls outside of this range, adjust the mass of unknown so that the 2nd and 3rd trials fall within this region. See the equation in Part A, step 10, to determine the proper sample size and approximate volume of $KMnO_4$ needed.

5. After performing a total of three trials using your unknown, perform the necessary calculations, time permitting, to see if the data are close. The easiest way to analyze your data is to divide the volume of $KMnO_4$ needed for each trial by the mass of the sample for that trial. Results for the mL/g ratio should agree in the first three significant figures. If not, and time permits, perform additional trials as needed.

6. When finished, discard the $KMnO_4$ solution in the sink, followed by lots of water. Rinse the storage bottle and all glassware thoroughly. Return the buret, and have your instructor sign your data sheet and lock your equipment drawer before leaving the laboratory.

IV. Calculations

NOTE: This procedure can produce very accurate results. You will be graded on both your calculations and the accuracy of your results. Be sure to pay close attention to significant figures to receive proper credit for your work.

Using the two half-reactions in the introduction, the electron transfer method can be used to obtain the balanced overall reaction. Use this balanced equation to determine the number of moles of iron(II) ion needed to react per mole of permanganate ion. This ratio will appear in several of the equations below, and must be determined by you from the balanced overall reaction.

The following relationship, based on the standardization titration, is used to determine the exact molarity of the $KMnO_4$ solution.

$$\text{moles Fe}^{2+} = \frac{(\text{moles MnO}_4^-)(\text{factor from equation in mol Fe}^{2+})}{\text{mol MnO}_4^-}$$

$$= \frac{\text{grams Fe}(NH_4)_2(SO_4)_2 \cdot 6\,H_2O}{\text{gram molar mass}} = (V_{KMnO_4})(M_{KMnO_4})(\text{factor from equation})$$

All of the quantities above are known, except for the molarity of the permanganate solution. When solving for M_{KMnO_4}, make sure the volume of $KMnO_4$ is in liters, and pay close attention to significant figures.

Average your results, and report both the average and the average deviation. The deviation is the (trial value) − (average value), and the average deviation is the sum of the absolute values of the deviation divided by the number of trials.

The amount of iron(II) in each sample is determined using the same equations as the standardization of $KMnO_4$, except the unknown in the equation has changed. Use the equation below, with the average value of the molarity of $KMnO_4$, and the volume of titrant in liters.

$$\text{moles Fe}^{2+} = (V_{KMnO_4})(M_{KMnO_4})(\text{factor from equation})$$

The amount of iron in your unknown should be reported as %Fe by mass. Convert the moles of Fe^{2+} to grams of Fe by multiplying by the atomic mass of iron (pay attention to significant figures). The %Fe in the sample is obtained by dividing the grams of Fe in the sample by the total mass of the sample and multiplying by 100%. Average the results and obtain the average deviation as previously explained. Lastly, the percent deviation in the %Fe can be calculated as follows:

$$\% \text{ deviation} = \frac{\text{average deviation}}{\text{average } \% \text{ Fe}} \times 100\%$$

[Report Form continued]

Name   Section #

I. Data
Record data in ink with units.

A. Standardization of KMnO$_4$

1. Mass of beaker + ferrous ammonium sulfate

	Before Transfer	After Transfer	Mass of Sample
Sample 1			
Sample 2			
Sample 3			

2. Buret Readings

	Initial Reading	Final Reading	Volumn KMnO$_4$
Sample 1			
Sample 2			
Sample 3			

II. Calculations
Show all of your work, where indicated, including any formulas, units, etc. Pay attention to significant figures.

A. 1. Using the two half-reactions in the introduction, balance the overall reaction which occurs between permanganate ion and iron(II). Show your method.

Balanced eqn: _____

2. From your balanced equation, how many moles of iron(II) react per mole of MnO_4^-? (This factor from the equation will be used in further calculations. **Transfer this factor to the laboratory report form for week two.**)

moles Fe^{2+}/moles $KMnO_4$ = _____

B. Calculation of the molarity of $KMnO_4$. Show sample calculation—Trial 1.

   1. Moles ferrous ammonium sulfate in sample 1.

   2. Moles $KMnO_4$ required to react with Fe^{2+} in sample 1.

   3. Molarity of $KMnO_4$ based on Trial 1.

   4. Results:

	Molarity $KMnO_4$	Deviation
Trial 1		
Trial 2		
Trial 3		
Average		

Transfer the average molarity to the report form for week 2, and to your storage bottle.

[Report Form continued]

Name	Section #

III. Questions

1. Why is it permissible to use a wet bottle when first obtaining your $KMnO_4$ solution? Be specific.

2. If a small amount of ferrous ammonium sulfate is spilled when transferring it from the beaker to the Erlenmeyer flask, how will this affect the calculated molarity of $KMnO_4$? Explain your answer.

I. Data (Week 2)

Record data in ink, with units.

A. Results from Standardization of $KMnO_4$ (Week 1)

1. moles Fe^{2+}/moles $KMnO_4$ = _____ (from previous report form)

2. Molarity of $KMnO_4$ = _____ (from previous report form)

B. Determination of Iron(II) in Unknown

1. Unknown # _____

2. Mass of unknown samples—vial and contents

	Before Transfer	After Transfer	Mass of Sample
Sample 1			
Sample 2			
Sample 3			

3. Buret readings

	Initial Reading	Final Reading	Volume KMnO$_4$
Sample 1			
Sample 2			
Sample 3			

II. Calculations

Show sample calculations for unknown Trial 1. Use the average M KMnO$_4$ from the previous report. Pay attention to significant figures.

A. Calculation of %Fe in Unknown

1. Moles of KMnO$_4$ reacted in unknown Trial 1.

2. Moles Fe^{2+} in unknown sample 1.

[Report Form continued]

Name   Section #

3. Mass of Fe in unknown sample 1.

4. % Fe by mass in unknown sample 1.

5. Summary of Results:

	Moles Fe^{2+}	grams Fe	% Fe	Deviation
Sample 1				
Sample 2				
Sample 3				
Average				

III. Questions

1. Why is the $KMnO_4$ solution first reacted with ferrous ammonium sulfate before being used to titrate the unknown?

2. What volume of a 0.2070 M $KMnO_4$ solution will be needed to completely oxidize a 1.1035 gram sample of $FeSO_4 \cdot 7\ H_2O$? Clearly show all of your calculations.

Experiment 16

Kinetics of the Iodine Clock Reaction

I. Introduction

The kinetics of the following reaction will be studied in this experiment.

$$5\,HSO_3^-{}_{(aq)} + 2\,IO_3^-{}_{(aq)} \rightarrow I_{2(aq)} + 5\,SO_4^{2-}{}_{(aq)} + 3\,H^+{}_{(aq)} + H_2O_{(l)}$$

Specifically, you will determine the dependence of the rate on the concentration of iodate ion.

The *rate law* for the reaction cannot be predicted from the chemical equation, and must be determined experimentally. For the above reaction, the rate law will have the form:

$$Rate = k[HSO_3^-]^x[IO_3^-]^y$$

In this experiment you will determine the value of the exponent y by reacting varying amounts of iodate ion with a fixed amount of bisulfite ion. The reaction time of each mixture will be measured, and the order of the reaction with respect to iodate determined graphically.

In order to measure the rate of the reaction, a small amount of starch has been added to the bisulfite solution. When the above reaction occurs and produces enough elemental iodine, the iodine will react with the starch to form a blue-black color. This sudden change of color from colorless to blue-black is easily observed, and serves as an "indicator" that the reaction has progressed to produce enough iodine to change the color of the reaction mixture. In this way, the reaction time is easily measured with a stopwatch or a clock with a second hand.

II. Equipment Needed

This experiment requires the following:

- 150 mL beaker
- 50 mL graduated cylinder
- 500 mL beaker
- 2 watch glasses
- several small beakers
- 100 mL beaker
- pipet and rubber bulb (from instructor)
- watch/clock with second hand

III. Procedure

NOTE: This reaction is extremely sensitive to the presence of impurities. All glassware must be thoroughly cleaned before proceeding. You will be performing the same reaction, using different amounts of reagents, several times during the course of the experiment. Your 100 or 150 mL beakers are the most convenient size to use for this procedure. They must be **cleaned and dried before each use**. Obtain a large beaker of distilled water and a small beaker of soap to be used for the cleaning of glassware.

1. Clean your largest beaker, fill it with distilled water, and allow it to reach room temperature. This water will be used in several reaction mixtures described below. In separate clean dry beakers obtain 85 mL of stock bisulfite solution and 450 mL of stock iodate solution. Label the beakers and cover them with a watch glass. Record the exact concentrations of each solution on the data sheet.

2. Obtain a thermometer from your instructor and measure and record the temperature of the solutions to the nearest 0.1°C.

3. Obtain a pipet from your instructor, and clean it with soap followed by tap water and then distilled water rinses. Pour approximately 8 mL of the stock bisulfite solution into a small beaker. Rinse the pipet three times with small portions (2–3 mL each) of the bisulfite stock solution in the small beaker.

4. Pipet exactly 5.00 mL of fresh bisulfite stock solution into a clean and dry 100 mL beaker.

5. Measure 50.0 mL of stock iodate solution using a graduated cylinder.

6. Make sure a clock or watch with a second hand is available. You must start timing as soon as you start adding the contents of the graduated cylinder to the beaker containing the 5.00 mL of bisulfite solution. While stirring constantly, measure the time required, in seconds, for the solution to turn blue. (It will take 30–60 seconds.)

7. Repeat steps 4–6 above to perform a second trial.

8. You will measure the rate of reaction of four other reaction mixtures. In each case, exactly 5.00 mL of stock bisulfite ion should be pipetted into a clean dry beaker or flask. Use a graduated cylinder to measure the quantities of iodate solution and distilled water listed below into another clean dry beaker. Mix the iodate and distilled water thoroughly, and start timing as soon as you start to add the iodate solution to the 5.00 mL of bisulfite solution. (Do **not** add the bisulfite to the iodate.) Stir all reaction mixtures constantly, and record the time, in seconds, at which the blue color appears. All trials should be done in duplicate to minimize errors in measurement. The five reaction mixtures to be studied are tabulated below.

Mixture	Stock HSO_3^-	Stock IO_3^-	H_2O
1	5.00 mL	50.0 mL	0.0 mL (steps 4–6)
2	5.00 mL	40.0 mL	10.0 mL
3	5.00 mL	30.0 mL	20.0 mL
4	5.00 mL	20.0 mL	30.0 mL
5	5.00 mL	10.0 mL	40.0 mL

9. After performing each reaction twice, return the pipet and bulb to your instructor and have your instructor sign your data sheet and lock your equipment drawer before leaving the laboratory.

IV. Calculations

The reaction order with respect to iodate ion will be determined graphically. Since two trials were performed for each reaction mixture, average the reaction times before performing further calculations or graphing.

The rate law of the reaction, as stated in the introduction, will have the form:

$$\text{Rate} = k[HSO_3^-]^x[IO_3^-]^y$$

Since the total volume of the reaction mixture and the volume of stock bisulfite are the same for each reaction, the term $k[HSO_3^-]^x$ remains constant for all reaction mixtures. Thus, under the experimental conditions, the rate law simplifies to:

$$\text{Rate} = \text{constant}[IO_3^-]^y$$

This relationship shows that the rate will be directly proportional to the iodate concentration raised to the y power. The rate of the reaction is inversely proportional to the reaction time. That is, a slow rate will have a high (long) reaction time, and a fast rate will have a low (short) reaction time.

$$\text{Rate } \alpha \text{ (time)}^{-1}$$

Combining this relationship with the one above it, we get:

$$(\text{time})^{-1} = \text{constant}[IO_3^-]^y$$

Taking the log of both sides, this equation becomes:

$$-\log(\text{time}) = y \log[IO_3^-] + \log \text{constant}$$

This form of the equation is in linear (y=mx+b) form. If the negative log of the reaction time is graphed versus $\log[IO_3^-]$, a straight line should be obtained. The slope of the line equals y, the order of the reaction with respect to iodate. You will construct such a graph. Make sure you follow the general graphing guidelines in the appendix of this manual.

You can calculate the $[IO_3^-]$ for each reaction as follows:

$$[IO_3^-] = (V_{\text{iodate}})(M_{\text{iodate}})/\text{total volume}$$

Graph the log of iodate concentration on the x-axis, and $-\log(\text{reaction time})$ on the y-axis. When taking the logarithm of a number, the resulting log should have as many places after the decimal as significant figures in the original number. For example, a reaction time with two significant figures would have a log with two places after the decimal. Be sure to use proper (mm grid) paper and choose an appropriate scale. Indicate on the graph the points used to calculate the slope. Keep in mind that the value of y (the reaction order) is usually a small whole number, while the slope of the line may be close to, but not equal to, a whole number.

[Report Form]

Name		Section #

Instructor's Signature		Date

I. Data

Record data in ink with units.

A. Concentration of Reagents

[stock HSO_3^-] = _____   [stock IO_3^-] = _____

B. Reaction Times

Mixture	Trial 1	Trial 2	Average Time (seconds)
1			
2			
3			
4			
5			

II. Calculations

Show a sample calculation for reaction mixture #3. Show any equations and units.

A. Calculation of [IO_3^-] in mixture #3.

III. Tabulation of Data for Graph

A. Graph to Determine Reaction Order

Mixture	−log(time)	$[IO_3^-]$	$log[IO_3^-]$
1			
2			
3			
4			
5			

Attach your graph of −log(time) versus $log[IO_3^-]$ to this report form. Make sure you followed the general graphing guidelines in the appendix and have shown the points used for determining the slope.

IV. Results

A. Determination of the Reaction Order for Iodate Ion

1. Show the calculation of the slope of the line.

slope = _____

2. The value of y in the rate law is _____

V. Questions

1. Why must the beakers used to carry out each reaction be completely dry? Be specific.

[Report Form continued]

Name   Section #

2. Use your value of y obtained in this experiment to answer this question. Remember that y should be an integer. If you double the concentration of iodate ion, what will happen to the reaction time? Explain your answer.

3. Use your graph to answer this question. Assuming the same temperature and concentration of bisulfite ion, what concentration of iodate ion would be needed to have a reaction time of 1 minute 25 seconds? Indicate the point on your graph used to answer this question. Show any calculations below.

172

Experiment 17

Spectrophotometric Study of an Equilibrium Reaction

I. Introduction

This experiment will study the possible equilibrium reactions between aqueous Fe^{3+} and the thiocyanate ion, SCN^-. In water, iron(III) becomes hydrated with six water molecules to form $Fe(H_2O)_6^{3+}$. Depending on the experimental conditions, the aqueous ion reacts with thiocyanate to replace anywhere from 1 to 6 of the water molecules. The iron-thiocyanate complex is intensely colored, and its concentration can be determined spectrophotometrically. A more detailed discussion of the theory of spectrophotometry can be found in the introduction to the *Spectrophotometric Determination of Dyes* experiment in this manual.

Several solutions containing known amounts of iron(III) ion and thiocyanate ion will be prepared, and the concentration of the resulting iron-thiocyanate complex will be determined using a Spectronic 20 and a Beer's law plot. Three possible reactions between the iron(III) ion and thiocyanate ion will be considered. These are:

1. $Fe^{3+}_{(aq)} + SCN^- \rightleftharpoons Fe(SCN)^{2+}_{(aq)}$ $\qquad K_{eq} = \dfrac{\left[Fe(SCN)^{2+}\right]}{\left[Fe^{3+}\right]\left[SCN^-\right]}$

2. $Fe^{3+}_{(aq)} + 2\,SCN^- \rightleftharpoons Fe(SCN)_2^+_{(aq)}$ $\qquad K_{eq} = \dfrac{\left[Fe(SCN)_2^+\right]}{\left[Fe^{3+}\right]\left[SCN^-\right]^2}$

3. $Fe^{3+}_{(aq)} + 4\,SCN^- \rightleftharpoons Fe(SCN)_4^-_{(aq)}$ $\qquad K_{eq} = \dfrac{\left[Fe(SCN)_4^-\right]}{\left[Fe^{3+}\right]\left[SCN^-\right]^4}$

Since known amounts of iron(III) and thiocyanate will be mixed, and the concentration of the iron-thiocyanate complex determined spectrophotometrically, it will be possible to calculate the equilibrium constant for each of the three possible equilibrium reactions above. The reaction which gives a constant value of K_{eq} for all the solutions prepared will be the correct one under the experimental conditions.

II. Equipment Needed

This experiment requires the following:

- 10 mL Mohr pipet and rubber bulb (from instructor)
- 5 – 125 × 15 mm (medium) test tubes
- 2 – 50 mL beakers
- several small beakers
- 2 – 250 mL beakers
- wash bottle
- stirring rod
- Kimwipes
- test tube rack

III. Procedure

Each solution will be prepared using a Mohr pipet for all volume measurements. For accurate results, the pipet must be rinsed with small portions of the solution to be measured before filling. In this way, the solution to be measured will not be diluted or wasted. You will be measuring out quantities of both solutions and distilled water into each test tube.

1. Clean and dry five 125 × 15 mm (medium) test tubes. Label them 1–5.

2. Obtain a 10 mL Mohr (graduated) pipet and a pipet bulb from your instructor. Thoroughly clean the pipet first with soap solution by drawing up small portions (1–2 mL) of soap using the pipet bulb. Then rinse with tap water. Rinse with several small portions of distilled water by drawing approximately 3 mL of water into the pipet using the bulb. If the pipet has been properly cleaned, it will drain without leaving droplets of water on the inner surfaces of the pipet.

3. Using clean dry labeled beakers, obtain approximately 40 mL of 0.00200 M iron(III) nitrate (in 0.5 M HNO_3) stock solution and 35 mL of 0.00200 M KSCN stock solution. Also fill a beaker with distilled water.

4. Pour approximately 8 mL of the 0.00200 M iron(III) solution into a small beaker and rinse the pipet by drawing up small portions of the solution using the rubber bulb. With 2–3 mL in the pipet, remove the bulb, cover the tip with your finger, and tilt the pipet to coat the walls. Discard rinsings down the sink. After three

rinsings, fill the pipet using a fresh portion of the Fe^{3+} solution. Fill the pipet by squeezing the bulb, placing it over the top opening of the pipet, and releasing the bulb. **Do not let the solution go into the bulb.** Once the liquid level is near the top volume markings on the pipet, remove the bulb and cover the top opening with your index finger. You can gently release the pressure of your finger to release liquid from the pipet.

Write down the initial reading, and transfer exactly 5.00 mL of Fe^{3+} solution to each test tube. Rinse the pipet thoroughly with distilled water after adding the 5.00 mL of solution to all 5 test tubes.

5. Pipet 3.00 mL of water into the first test tube. Pipet the following volumes of water for the other test tubes.

Test Tube	mL H_2O
Tube #2	2.00 mL
Tube #3	1.50 mL
Tube #4	1.00 mL
Tube #5	0.50 mL

6. Pour approximately 8 mL of 0.00200 M KSCN solution into a small beaker, and rinse the pipet as previously described. After three rinsings, fill the pipet with a fresh portion of the KSCN solution, and deliver the following volumes of solution to each test tube.

Test Tube	mL KSCN
Tube #1	2.00 mL
Tube #2	3.00 mL
Tube #3	3.50 mL
Tube #4	4.00 mL
Tube #5	4.50 mL

7. Stir the first solution using a clean dry stirring rod. Rinse the rod, discarding washings in the sink, dry with Kimwipes, and stir the second solution. Stir all five solutions making sure to rinse and dry the stir rod in between.

8. Take your test tube rack, Kimwipes, a wash bottle, waste beaker, and your lab manual and pen to the spectrophotometer. The "solvent" cell should be filled with 0.002 M KSCN, and the wavelength should be set to 460 nm.

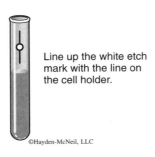

Line up the white etch mark with the line on the cell holder.

©Hayden-McNeil, LLC

Figure 17-1. Line up the white etch mark with the line on the cell holder.

9. Following the instructions in the appendix (also located near the spectropho-
    tometer), standardize the instrument for 0% and 100% transmittance. When in-
    serting the special cells (called cuvettes) into the sample holder, make sure the
    etching on the cell lines up with the mark on the holder. The cell should be filled
    only halfway. Be sure to wipe the outside with a Kimwipe and to handle the cell
    on the top half only.

10. Starting with the most dilute solution, rinse the solution cell with a small portion
    of solution #1. Fill the cell halfway with the solution, wipe the outside of the cell
    with a Kimwipe, and insert it in the cell holder. Read and record the % trans-
    mittance of the solution on the data sheet. When making measurements, stand
    directly in front of the meter to avoid parallax. Use the mirror on the scale to be
    sure you are standing in the proper position. The reflection of the needle should
    be obscured by the needle when you're in the correct position. Remove the cell,
    restandardize the instrument, and take a second reading of the % transmittance
    of solution #1 and record your results.

11. Discard the contents of the cell in the waste beaker, and repeat the rinsing, filling,
    and wiping of the cell with solution #2. Restandardize the instrument, and read
    and record the % transmittance of the solution. Make a second measurement, be-
    ing sure to standardize the instrument between all readings. Repeat this step with
    solutions 3–5. After your last measurement, rinse the solution cell with distilled
    water.

12. Clean the pipet and return it, along with the bulb, to your instructor. Discard the
    contents of the waste beaker in the sink.

13. Have your instructor sign your data sheet and lock your equipment drawer be-
    fore leaving the laboratory.

IV. Calculations

For a detailed discussion of spectrophotometry and Beer's law, see the introduction
section of the experiment entitled, *Spectrophotometric Determination of Dyes*.

The absorbance of each solution can be calculated from the average % transmittance
by the following equation.

$$A = \log\left(\frac{100}{\%T}\right) = 2 - \log \%T$$

When taking the logarithm of a number, the resulting log should have as many places after the decimal as significant figures in the original number. For example, a sample with a % transmittance of 26.3 (3 significant figures) has an absorbance of:

$$A = 2 - \log 26.3 = 2 - 1.420 = 0.580 \text{ (3 places after the decimal)}$$

Once the absorbance of each solution has been calculated, the concentration of the colored iron-thiocyanate complex can be determined using a Beer's law plot. Graph the data below to construct a Beer's law plot for the iron-thiocyanate complexes. Use the graph to determine the concentration (in moles/liter) which corresponds to the observed absorbance of each solution. This is the concentration of iron-thiocyanate complex formed in each test tube after equilibrium has been reached.

Data for the Beer's law plot follows. Graph the data following the general graphing guidelines in the appendix and the specific guidelines in the experiment entitled *Spectrophotometric Determination of Dyes*. This graph will be used to determine the concentration of the iron-thiocyanate complex in each of the solutions you prepare.

[iron(III)-thiocyanate complex]	Absorbance
3.088×10^{-5} M	0.152
6.176×10^{-5} M	0.307
9.264×10^{-5} M	0.443
1.235×10^{-4} M	0.587
1.544×10^{-4} M	0.752
1.853×10^{-4} M	0.891

Since the initial concentrations and the exact volumes of $Fe^{3+}_{(aq)}$ solution and $SCN^-_{(aq)}$ solution are known, it is possible, using each of the three reactions proposed, to calculate the molarity (i.e., equilibrium concentrations) of $Fe^{3+}_{(aq)}$ and $SCN^-_{(aq)}$ left in solution. Since the equilibrium concentrations of all three species appearing in the chemical equations are known, K_{eq} can be calculated for all three postulated reactions. The reaction which yields similar values of K_{eq} for all five solutions is the reaction which occurred under these experimental conditions.

A sample calculation will be provided for all three possible reactions for solution #1. Suppose solution #1 was placed in a spectrophotometer, its % transmittance measured, its absorbance calculated, and the corresponding concentration of iron-thiocyanate product found to be 4.8×10^{-5} M using the Beer's law plot.

We can calculate the initial concentrations of Fe^{3+} and SCN^{1-} for the solution as follows.

$$\text{initial concentration in solution} = \frac{(V_{stock})(M_{stock})}{(\text{Volume of solution})}$$

The volume of each component contained in solution #1 is:

0.00200 M KSCN	2.00 mL
0.00200 M Fe(NO$_3$)$_3$	5.00 mL
distilled water	3.00 mL
Total Volume	10.00 mL

The initial [SCN$^-$] is:

$$\frac{(2.00 \text{ mL})(0.00200 \text{ M})}{(10.00 \text{ mL})} = 4.00 \times 10^{-4} \text{ M}$$

The initial [Fe^{3+}] is:

$$\frac{(5.00 \text{ mL})(0.00200 \text{ M})}{(10.00 \text{ mL})} = 1.00 \times 10^{-3} \text{ M}$$

Since the absorbance indicates an equilibrium concentration of iron-thiocyanium product of 4.8×10^{-5} M, the equilibrium concentrations of Fe^{3+} and SCN^{1-} must decrease according to the stoichiometry of the possible reactions.

For reaction 1, the concentration of both reactants will decrease by one mole/liter for every mole/liter of product formed. That is, the reaction is 1:1:1 for Fe^{3+}: SCN$^-$:product.

$$1) \ Fe^{3+}_{(aq)} + SCN^- \rightleftharpoons Fe(SCN)^{2+}_{(aq)} \quad K_{eq} = \frac{\left[Fe(SCN)^{2+}\right]}{\left[Fe^{3+}\right]\left[SCN^-\right]}$$

The equilibrium concentrations of iron(III) and SCN$^-$ are:

$$\left[Fe^{3+}\right]_{eq} = \left[Fe^{3+}\right]_{init} - \left[Fe(SCN)^{2+}\right]_{eq} = .00100 - .000048 = 9.52 \times 10^{-4} \text{ M}$$

$$\left[SCN^-\right]_{eq} = \left[SCN^-\right]_{init} - \left[Fe(SCN)^{2+}\right]_{eq} = .00100 - .000048 = 3.52 \times 10^{-4} \text{ M}$$

Note that these calculations don't comply with rules about significant figures. Since a qualitative decision is to be made (that is, which reaction gives a constant value for K_{eq}), it is easiest to express all concentrations multiplied by 10^4 and expressed to two places after the decimal.

$$\text{For solution \#1, reaction \#1, } K_{eq} = \frac{(4.8 \times 10^{-5})}{(9.52 \times 10^{-4})(3.52 \times 10^{-4})} = 143$$

For the same solution using reaction 2 as a basis, the stoichiometry will change the equilibrium concentrations of the SCN$^-$ ion.

$$2) \ Fe^{3+}_{(aq)} + 2 \ SCN^- \rightleftharpoons Fe(SCN)^+_{2 \ (aq)} \quad K_{eq} = \frac{\left[Fe(SCN)_2^+\right]}{\left[Fe^{3+}\right]\left[SCN^-\right]^2}$$

For this reaction, the equilibrium concentration of the reactants is as follows:

$$[Fe^{3+}]_{eq} = [Fe^{3+}]_{init} - [Fe(SCN)_2{}^+]_{eq} = .00100 - .000048 = 9.52 \times 10^{-4} M$$

$$[SCN^-]_{eq} = [SCN^-]_{init} - 2[Fe(SCN)_2{}^+]_{eq} = .000400 - .000096 = 3.04 \times 10^{-4} M$$

The factor of two in the calculation of $[SCN^-]_{eq}$ arises from the fact that 2 moles of thiocyanate ion react to form 1 mole of iron-thiocyanate product.

For solution #1, reaction #2, $K_{eq} = \dfrac{(4.8 \times 10^{-5})}{(9.52 \times 10^{-4})(3.04 \times 10^{-4})^2} = 5.45 \times 10^5$

Considering the third reaction,

$$3) \quad Fe^{3+}{}_{(aq)} + 4\ SCN^- \rightleftharpoons Fe(SCN)_4{}^-{}_{(aq)} \qquad K_{eq} = \dfrac{\left[Fe(SCN)_4{}^-\right]}{[Fe^{3+}][SCN^-]^4}$$

the equilibrium concentration of SCN^- is:

$$[SCN^-]_{eq} = [SCN^-]_{init} - 4[Fe(SCN)_4{}^-]_{eq}$$

because the reaction shows four moles of SCN^- reacting to form the iron-thiocyanate product. The equilibrium iron(III) ion concentration is unchanged.

$$[SCN^-]_{eq} = .000400 - 4(.000048) = 2.08 \times 10^{-4}, \text{ and}$$

$$K_{eq} = \dfrac{(4.8 \times 10^{-5})}{(9.52 \times 10^{-4})(2.08 \times 10^{-4})^4} = 2.69 \times 10^{13}$$

After calculating K_{eq} for each solution and each possible reaction, you should get relatively similar values for one of the reactions. This is the reaction which predominates under the experimental conditions.

180

[Report Form]

_____
Name   Section #

_____
Instructor's Signature   Date

I. Data
Record data in ink.

A. Percent Transmittance of Solutions

Solution	#1	#2	#3	#4	#5
% Trans.: Trial 1					
Trial 2					
Average:					

II. Calculations
Provide a sample calculation for solution #3. Include any equations, units, etc.

A. Absorbance—show the calculation for solution #3.

Abs. = _____

B. Concentration of product (from Beer's law plot)—Attach the graph.

[product] = _____

C. $[Fe^{3+}]_{init}$ **in solution #3.**

$$[Fe^{3+}]_{init} = _____$$

D. $[SCN^-]_{init}$ **in solution #3.**

$$[SCN^-]_{init} = _____$$

E. $[Fe^{3+}]_{eq}$ **in solution #3.**

$$[Fe^{3+}]_{eq} = _____$$

F. Calculations based on reaction 1.

$$Fe^{3+}_{(aq)} + SCN^- \rightleftharpoons Fe(SCN)^{2+}_{(aq)}, \text{ for solution #3.}$$

1. $[SCN^-]_{eq}$ in solution #3 using reaction 1.

$$[SCN^-]_{eq} \text{ using reaction 1} = _____$$

[Report Form continued]

Name	Section #

2. K_{eq} for solution #3 using reaction 1.

$$K_{eq} = \text{_____}$$

G. Calculations based on reaction 2.

$$Fe^{3+}_{(aq)} + 2\, SCN^- \rightleftharpoons Fe(SCN)_2^{+}_{(aq)}, \text{ for solution #3.}$$

1. $[SCN^-]_{eq}$ in solution #3 using reaction 2.

$$[SCN^-]_{eq} \text{ using reaction 2} = \text{_____}$$

2. K_{eq} for solution #3 using reaction 2.

$$K_{eq} = \text{_____}$$

H. Calculations based on equation 3.

$$Fe^{3+}_{(aq)} + 4\,SCN^- \rightleftharpoons Fe(SCN)_4^-{}_{(aq)}, \text{ for solution \#3.}$$

1. $[SCN^-]_{eq}$ in solution #3 using reaction 3.

$[SCN^-]_{eq}$ using reaction 2 = _____

2. K_{eq} for solution #3 using reaction 3.

K_{eq} = _____

III. Summary of Results and Conclusions

A. Based on reaction 1: $Fe^{3+}_{(aq)} + SCN^- \rightleftharpoons Fe(SCN)^{2+}_{(aq)}$

Soln	Initial × 10^{+4}		%T	Abs.	Equilibrium × 10^{+4}			K_{eq}
	$[Fe^{3+}]$	$[SCN^-]$			*$[Fe(SCN)^{2+}]$	$[Fe^{3+}]$	$[SCN^-]$	
1								
2								
3								
4								
5								

*From the Beer's law plot

[Report Form continued]

Name   Section #

B. Based on reaction 2: $Fe^{3+}_{(aq)} + 2\,SCN^- \rightleftharpoons Fe(SCN)_2^{+}_{(aq)}$

| Soln | *Initial × 10^{+4} | | *%T | *Abs. | Equilibrium × 10^{+4} | | | K$_{eq}$ |
	[Fe^{3+}]	[SCN$^-$]			*[Fe(SCN)$_2^+$]	[Fe^{3+}]	[SCN$^-$]	
1								
2								
3								
4								
5								

*These are the same regardless of the reaction.

C. Based on reaction 3: $Fe^{3+}_{(aq)} + 4\,SCN^- \rightleftharpoons Fe(SCN)_4^{-}_{(aq)}$

| Soln | *Initial × 10^{+4} | | *%T | *Abs. | Equilibrium × 10^{+4} | | | K$_{eq}$ |
	[Fe^{3+}]	[SCN$^-$]			*[Fe(SCN)$_4^-$]	[Fe^{3+}]	[SCN$^-$]	
1								
2								
3								
4								
5								

*These are the same regardless of the reaction.

D. Based on your results, which reaction occurs under the experimental conditions? Explain your answer.

E. **What is the average value of K_{eq} for the reaction which occurs? Show your calculations.**

average K_{eq} = _____

IV. Questions

1. This experiment was performed with an excess of Fe^{3+} over SCN^- in most of the solutions. If a large excess of SCN^- had been used instead, which reaction might have predominated? Explain your answer.

18 Experiment

Le Châtelier's Principle

I. Introduction

This experiment involves the observation of several reactions which are in equilibrium. The reactions are such that the reactants and products have different appearances (color, solubility, etc.), so that a shift of the equilibrium can be observed with the eye. According to Le Châtelier's principle, when a stress is applied to a system in equilibrium, the system will adjust so as to counteract that stress. The stress can be the addition or removal of reactants or products, a change in temperature, the removal or addition of solvent, a change in pressure, etc. The effect of several of these stresses will be observed for a variety of reactions. Parts of this experiment will be done in microscale, that is, using very small quantities of solutions and solids. Most reactions will be performed in an assay plate, a plastic dish containing many wells, and most solutions will be measured using eyedroppers and counting the number of drops, rather than with a graduated cylinder.

You will be required to write down your observations for each reaction studied. Things to look for are changes in color, the formation of a solid (precipitate), the formation of a gas (bubbling), etc. Be precise in your language. For example, clear and colorless are not the same. Clear means translucent and easy to see through, but it may also be colored. The opposite of clear is cloudy, or opaque and difficult to see through. Just as the sky can be clear and blue, a solution can be clear and colored. Pure water is both clear and colorless.

II. Equipment Needed

This experiment requires the following:

- 24-well assay plate

- several clean droppers

III. Procedure

This experiment involves the study of several reactions in equilibrium. They may be performed in any order. You may use a regular-sized dropper for all parts of the procedure unless otherwise specified. Make sure the dropper is rinsed with distilled water before each change of solutions. Most reactions can be better observed if the assay plate is placed on a piece of white paper rather than the benchtop. Stirring of the wells can be accomplished by placing the plate on the benchtop and gently moving the plate in a circular motion.

In many steps of the procedure you are directed to add a reagent dropwise until a change is observed. If you have added ten drops of a solution and still have not observed a change, note this in your observations and go on to the next step in the procedure.

A. The Chromate-Dichromate Equilibrium

Chromate ion and dichromate ion exist in equilibrium with each other according to the following net ionic reaction.

$$2\,CrO_4^{2-}{}_{(aq)} + 2\,H^+{}_{(aq)} \rightleftharpoons Cr_2O_7^{2-}{}_{(aq)} + H_2O_{(l)}$$

The conversion of one ion to the other is readily observed since the chromate ion is yellow in color, and dichromate is deep orange in color. In this part of the procedure, you will convert one ion to the other by the addition of a strong acid and a strong base.

1. Place enough of 1 M K_2CrO_4 in the well of a 24-well assay plate to cover the bottom of the well and observe and record the color. Add 3 M H_2SO_4 dropwise until a change is observed. Record your observation.

2. Using a clean dropper, add several drops of 6 M NaOH to the well in step 1 until a change is observed and record your observations. Add 3 M H_2SO_4 to see if the change is reversible.

B. The Iron(III)-Thiocyanate Ion Equilibrium

Ferric ion (Fe^{3+}) reacts with thiocyanate ion (SCN^-) to form a deeply colored red complex ion. A complex ion is an ion which results from the combination of other ions or molecules. Many transition metal ions form very stable complex ions, and often exist as complex ions in water. For example, the iron(III) ion in water is more correctly a complex ion containing one iron(III) ion and 6 water molecules. The reaction for the equilibrium between iron(III), thiocyanate ion, and the complex ion is:

$$Fe^{3+}_{(aq)} + SCN^-_{(aq)} \rightleftharpoons Fe(SCN)^{2+}_{(aq)}$$

If we consider the fact that $Fe^{3+}_{(aq)}$ more accurately exists as a complex ion, $Fe(H_2O)_6^{3+}$, the above reaction can be seen as a displacement or competition reaction where the thiocyanate ion displaces water from the iron(III) ion. The equilibrium reaction can thus be written more precisely as:

$$Fe(H_2O)_6^{3+}{}_{(aq)} + SCN^-_{(aq)} \rightleftharpoons Fe(H_2O)_5(SCN)^{2+}{}_{(aq)} + H_2O_{(l)}$$

1. Place 3 drops of 0.10 M $Fe(NO_3)_3$ and 3 drops of 0.10 M KSCN solution in the same well of a 24-well assay plate. Add distilled water to this mixture until it is dilute enough so that you can see through the solution. It should be dilute enough so that you will be able to observe decreases and increases in the intensity of the color. Using a dropper, place enough of the iron-thiocyanate solution to cover the bottom of each of 4 wells of a 24-well assay plate. Three of these wells will be used for reactions in steps 2–4 below. The fourth well will be used for comparison, and will not be reacted further.

2. To the first sample in a well, add some 0.10 M $Fe(NO_3)_3$ dropwise until a change is observed. Record your observations on the data sheet.

3. To the second sample of solution add some 0.10 M KSCN dropwise until a change is observed. Record your observations on the data sheet.

4. To the third sample of solution, add 0.10 M NaOH dropwise until a change is observed. Write down your observations. NOTE: $Fe(OH)_3$ is insoluble in water.

C. The Cobalt(II)-Chloride Ion Equilibrium

The cobalt(II) ion exists in water as a complex ion with six water molecules attached to the metal ion, $Co(H_2O)_6^{2+}$. This complex ion is pink in color. Chloride ion can displace the water molecules to form a new complex ion, $CoCl_4^{2-}$. The chloride complex is blue in color. You may have seen this reaction on humidity indicators. These are typically made of a strip of paper which has been dipped in a solution of cobalt(II) ion mixed with chloride ion. The strip of paper will be pink when the humidity is high and will gradually turn blue in color as the air becomes drier. The equilibrium reaction is:

$$Co(H_2O)_6^{2+}{}_{(aq)} + 4\,Cl^-_{(aq)} \rightleftharpoons CoCl_4^{2-}{}_{(aq)} + 6\,H_2O_{(l)}$$

1. Using your 24-well assay plate, place enough 0.10 M $CoCl_2$ (in alcohol) solution to cover the bottom of one well. Note and record the color of the solution.

2. To the well of $CoCl_2$ in the 24-well plate, add water dropwise using a micropipet until a color change is observed. Record your observations.

3. To the well containing $CoCl_2$ and water, carefully add some concentrated H_2SO_4 dropwise until a change is observed. Record your observations.

CAUTION: Concentrated sulfuric acid is extremely caustic. Flush all spills with lots of water followed by a solution of sodium bicarbonate. Report all spills immediately to your instructor.

NOTE: Concentrated sulfuric acid is a strong dehydrating agent. (It's very effective at removing water.)

D. The Equilibrium in a Saturated NaCl Solution

A saturated solution contains the maximum amount of solute which can be dissolved without solid solute precipitating out from solution. It is usually prepared by adding solute to solvent until excess solute remains undissolved, and then filtering the mixture. For a saturated solution of NaCl, which is 5.4 M, it undergoes the following equilibrium reaction between dissolved salt and excess solid.

$$Na^+_{(aq)} + Cl^-_{(aq)} \rightleftharpoons NaCl_{(s)}$$

In a saturated solution, even though no solid may be present, addition of compounds containing the ions of the saturated salt (called "common ions" because the compounds and the saturated salt have these ions in common) can cause precipitation. In this part of the experiment, chloride ion (from concentrated HCl) will be added to a saturated solution of NaCl.

1. Place enough saturated (5.4 M) NaCl to cover the bottom of each of two wells of a 24-well assay plate.

2. To one of the wells of saturated NaCl add several drops (count them) of concentrated (12 M) HCl until a change is observed. Record your observations. **CAUTION:** Concentrated HCl is extremely caustic. Wash any spills with lots of water and then with a sodium bicarbonate solution. Report all spills to your instructor.

3. To the other well of saturated NaCl add the same number of drops of dilute (3 M) HCl. Record your observations. **CAUTION:** HCl is caustic.

E. The Equilibrium of Saturated Barium Chromate

An insoluble salt can sometimes be dissolved if one of the ions can effectively be removed from solution due to a competing equilibrium reaction. In this part of the experiment you will prepare barium chromate, a relatively insoluble salt, by mixing barium chloride (a source of barium ions) and potassium chromate (a source of chromate ions). The net ionic equilibrium reaction is:

$$Ba^{2+}_{(aq)} + CrO_4^{2-}_{(aq)} \rightleftharpoons BaCrO_{4(s)}$$

According to Le Châtelier's principle, the solid barium chromate precipitate can be dissolved if the concentration of barium ion or chromate ion is lowered. The chromate ion concentration can be lowered by adding acid, since, as seen in Part A of the procedure, acid will convert the chromate ion to the dichromate ion.

1. In a well of the 24-well assay plate, mix 5 drops of 0.1 M $BaCl_2$ and 2 drops of 1 M K_2CrO_4. Record your observations.

2. Add 12 M HCl (**CAUTION:** HCl is caustic) dropwise until a change is observed and record your observations.

F. Equilibrium of Saturated Ferric Hydroxide

Most insoluble hydroxides can be dissolved by the reaction with acid. The acid serves the purpose of effectively removing hydroxide from the reaction mixture. The precipitate dissolves so as to replenish the hydroxide which was removed via reaction with the acid. In this part of the experiment, an insoluble hydroxide, $Fe(OH)_3$, will be prepared by reacting $Fe(NO_3)_3$ with NaOH. The net-ionic equilibrium reaction is:

$$Fe^{3+}_{(aq)} + 3\, OH^-_{(aq)} \rightleftharpoons Fe(OH)_{3(s)}$$

The iron(III) hydroxide can be dissolved if hydroxide ion or ferric ion are removed from solution by a competing reaction. One such reaction in which ferric ion can be removed occurs when more base is added to form the soluble complex ion $Fe(OH)_4^-$.

$$Fe^{3+}_{(aq)} + 4\, OH^-_{(aq)} \rightleftharpoons Fe(OH)_{4\,(aq)}^-$$

1. Place enough 0.10 M $Fe(NO_3)_3$ dropwise to cover the bottom of each of 2 wells in a 24-well assay plate. Add 6 M NaOH (**CAUTION:** NaOH is caustic) dropwise to each well until a precipitate forms. Record your observations.

2. Add 12 M HCl (**CAUTION!**) to one of the above wells until a change is observed. Record your observations.

3. To the other well from step 1 above, add additional 6 M NaOH until a change is observed (**CAUTION!**). Record your observations.

G. Equilibrium of Ammonia in Water

Ammonia in water acts as a weak base according to the following equilibrium reaction.

$$NH_{3(aq)} + H_2O_{(l)} \rightleftharpoons NH_4^+{}_{(aq)} + OH^-_{(aq)}$$

In this section of the experiment, you will observe the shifts of equilibrium in the above reaction by observing the color change of a solution of ammonia containing a drop of phenolphthalein. Phenolphthalein is an acid–base indicator which is faintly pink at a pH of approximately 9, bright pink at higher pH, and colorless in solutions with a pH below 9. All acid–base indicators are weak acids which undergo their own equilibrium reaction in water. The acidic (protonated) form of the indicator has a different color than the basic form. The general form of these equilibrium reactions is given below, where HIn represents the protonated form of the indicator (colorless for phenolphthalein) and In$^-$ represents the basic (pink) form of phenolphthalein.

$$HIn_{(aq)} + OH^-_{(aq)} \rightleftharpoons H_2O_{(l)} + In^-_{(aq)}$$

colorless   pink

In observing changes in a solution containing both ammonia and phenolphthalein, you will be seeing shifts in both of the above equilibrium reactions.

1. Place enough 0.10 M aqueous ammonia in each of three wells of a 24-well assay plate so that the bottom of the well is covered. Add 1 drop of phenolphthalein indicator to each well and record your observations.

2. To one of the wells containing the ammonia and phenolphthalein, add 3 M HCl dropwise until a change is observed. **CAUTION:** HCl is caustic. Record your observations.

3. To the second well of ammonia and phenolphthalein, add a crystal of solid ammonium chloride (NH_4Cl). Record your observations after the crystal has dissolved.

4. To the third well of ammonia and phenolphthalein, add 1 drop of .10 M NaOH. Record your observations. Then add additional .10 M HCl to see if the change is reversible.

H. Equilibrium of Saturated AgCl

Silver ion forms insoluble salts with many anions including those of the halogens (Cl$^-$, Br$^-$, and I$^-$). In this part of the procedure you will prepare a saturated solution of silver chloride and observe some related equilibrium reactions. The equilibrium reaction for AgCl is:

$$AgCl_{(s)} \rightleftharpoons Ag^+_{(aq)} + Cl^-_{(aq)}$$

Silver forms many insoluble salts (including the dull gray coating on silverware and jewelry) which can be easily dissolved in ammonia. Dissolution (dissolving) is brought about by the formation of a very stable complex ion containing silver ion and ammonia. The reaction is:

$$Ag^+_{(aq)} + 2\,NH_{3\,(aq)} \rightleftharpoons Ag(NH_3)_2^+_{(aq)}$$

Previously insoluble silver salts dissolve because the ammonia effectively removes free silver ion from solution and the salt dissolves so as to replenish the concentration of Ag$^+$.

1. Place enough 0.10 M $AgNO_3$ solution in a well of a 24-well assay plate so that the bottom of the well is covered and observe its color. Add 2 drops of 12 M HCl (**CAUTION!**), mix the contents, and record your observations.

2. Allow the contents of the well to settle. Once the solid has settled, take a narrow-tipped dropper and try to draw off a few drops of the liquid and place it in an adjacent well. Try to leave as much solid as possible in the original well.

3. Add two drops of a fresh sample of $AgNO_3$ to the drops of liquid which were transferred. Record your observations. Then add several drops of concentrated (15 M) NH_3 until a change is observed. Record your observations. **CAUTION:** Fumes from ammonia are noxious. Handle with care.

4. Add several drops of 15 M NH_3 (**CAUTION**) to the well containing the solid. Record your observations. Then add several drops of 6 M HNO_3 to determine if the reaction is reversible. **CAUTION:** Nitric acid is extremely caustic. Wash all spills immediately with lots of water.

After completing all parts of the procedure, dispose of all chemicals down the sink, followed by lots of water, and thoroughly clean the assay plate. Have your instructor sign your data sheet and lock your equipment drawer before leaving the laboratory.

IV. The Laboratory Report

Fill in all items asked for on the report sheets. For each reaction you are to write the equilibrium reaction being studied, your observations upon applying a "stress" to the system, and how that stress shifts the equilibrium in one direction or the other.

194

[Report Form]

Name   Section #

Instructor's Signature   Date

For each part of the procedure, describe the color of each solution and your observations as solutions were mixed. Items will be numbered to correspond with the numbers in the procedure section. A "stress" can be the addition or removal of a product or reactant, a change in pressure or temperature, etc. Be specific when identifying the stress, such as "addition of H^+ ions" rather than "the addition of sulfuric acid" as in the case of Part A1 of the procedure.

I. Observations and Conclusions
Record data in ink.

A. Chromate/Dichromate Equilibrium

	Equilibrium Reaction:			
	K_2CrO_4 (A1)	H_2SO_4 (A1)	K_2CrO_4 and H_2SO_4 (A1)	K_2CrO_4, H_2SO_4, and NaOH (A2)
Observations: (colors, precipitates, etc.)				
"Stress" applied:				
Direction of equilibrium shift: (to the left, right, or neither)				

Was the shift observed when NaOH was added reversed by adding more H_2SO_4?

How does the addition of NaOH, which does not appear in the equilibrium reaction, affect the reaction between chromate ion and dichromate ion? Explain your answer and include any relevant chemical reactions.

B. Iron(III)/Thiocyanate Equilibrium

	Equilibrium Reaction:					
	$Fe(NO_3)_3$ (B1)	KSCN (B1)	$Fe(NO_3)_3$ /KSCN (B1)	$Fe(NO_3)_3$/KSCN mixture plus		
				$Fe(NO_3)_3$ (B2)	KSCN (B3)	NaOH (B4)
Observations: (colors, precipitates, etc.)						
"Stress" applied:						
Direction of equilibrium shift: (to the left, right, or neither)						

[Report Form continued]

Name   Section #

C. Cobalt(II)/Chloride Ion Equilibrium

Equilibrium Reaction:		
$CoCl_2$ (step C1) in alcohol	$CoCl_2 + H_2O$ (C2)	$CoCl_2 + H_2O + H_2SO_4$ (C3)
Observations: (colors, precipitates, etc.)		
"Stress" applied:		
Direction of equilibrium shift: (to the left, right, or neither)		

Sulfuric acid does not appear in the equilibrium reaction. Explain how its presence in the reaction mixture influences the direction of the equilibrium.

D. Saturated NaCl Equilibrium

Equilibrium Reaction:			
	Sat'd NaCl (D1)	Sat'd NaCl + 12 M HCl (D2)	Sat'd NaCl + 3 M HCl (D3)
Observations: (colors, precipitates, etc.)			
"Stress" applied:			
Direction of equilibrium shift: (to the left, right, or neither)			

Explain the differences you observed when adding concentrated 12 M HCl and 3 M HCl to the saturated NaCl solution. (Hint: Saturated NaCl is 5.4 M.)

E. The Barium Ion/Chromate Ion Equilibrium

Equilibrium Reaction:				
	$BaCl_2$ (E1)	K_2CrO_4 (E1)	$BaCl_2$ + K_2CrO_4 (E1)	$BaCl_2$ + K_2CrO_4 + HCl (E2)
Observations: (colors, precipitates, etc.)				
"Stress" applied:				
Direction of equilibrium shift: (to the left, right, or neither)				

[Report Form continued]

Name _____   Section # _____

HCl does not appear in the equilibrium reaction between barium ion and chromate ion, yet it affects the reaction. Explain, making sure to use any relevant chemical equations.

Do you think $BaCrO_4$ is more soluble in acidic or in neutral solutions? Explain your answer using relevant chemical reactions.

F. Saturated Ferric Hydroxide Equilibrium

	Equilibrium Reaction:				
	$Fe(NO_3)_3$ (F1)	NaOH (F1)	$Fe(NO_3)_3$ + NaOH (F1)	$Fe(NO_3)_3$/NaOH plus	
				HCl (F2)	add'nl NaOH (F3)
Observations: (colors, precipitates, etc.)					
"Stress" applied:					
Direction of equilibrium shift: (to the left, right, or neither)					

Hydrochloric acid does not appear in the equilibrium reaction, yet it influences the reaction. Explain how it affects the reaction between iron and hydroxide ion. Be specific, and include any relevant chemical equations.

Write the reaction for ferric hydroxide dissolving in NaOH. HINT: Combine the two equilibrium reactions.

G. The NH_3/NH_4^+ Equilibrium

	Equilibrium Reaction:					
		NH_3 + phenolphthalein				
	NH_3 (E1)	only (G1)	+ HCl (G2)	+ NH_4Cl (G3)	+ NaOH (G4)	+ HCl (G4)
Observations: (colors, precipitates, etc.)						
"Stress" applied:						
Direction of equilibrium shift: (to the left, right, or neither)						

[Report Form continued]

Hydrochloric acid does not appear in either equilibrium reaction, yet it influences the reactions. Explain how it affects the equilibrium of ammonia and phenolphthalein in water and brings about the observed color change. Be specific, and include any relevant chemical equations.

H. Equilibria of Saturated AgCl

	Equilibrium Reaction:						
	$AgNO_3$ (H1)	HCl (H1)	$AgNO_3$ + HCl (H2)	Liquid + $AgNO_3$ (H3)	Liquid, $AgNO_3$ + NH_3 (H3)	Solid + NH_3 (H4)	Solid NH_3 + HNO_3 (H4)
Observations: (colors, precipitates, etc.)							
"Stress" applied:							
Direction of equilibrium shift: (to the left, right, or neither)							

Nitric acid does not appear in the equilibrium reaction involving silver ion and ammonia, yet it influences the reaction. Explain how it affects the equilibrium. Be specific, and include any relevant chemical equations.

202

19 Experiment

The Equivalent Weight of an Acid

I. Introduction

NOTE: This is a two-week experiment. If you missed the first week, see your instructor so that a standard solution of NaOH can be obtained for you.

In this experiment you will experimentally determine the *equivalent weight* of an unknown acid. The equivalent weight of an acid is that amount of acid (in grams) which will provide one mole of protons when reacted with a base. The equivalent weight of the acid will be determined using the technique of a *titration*. (Examples of acid–base titrations can be found in your textbook.) In a titration, known amounts of one reactant are reacted with an unknown amount of the other reactant until the chemical reaction between the two is complete. An indicator, in this case a substance which changes color, shows when the reaction is complete. At this point, called the *endpoint*, the amount of base reacted should equal the amount of acid reacted. For acid–base reactions, the neutralization reaction is (in net-ionic form):

$$H^+_{(aq)} + OH^-_{(aq)} \rightarrow H_2O_{(l)}$$

At the endpoint, the total number of moles of hydroxide reacted should equal the total number of moles of protons available from the acid. So, if the exact amount of base reacted (that is, its concentration and its volume) is known, the amount of acid present in the sample can be calculated.

In this procedure, NaOH solution will be used as the base. Since solid sodium hydroxide readily absorbs moisture from the air, it is not possible to weigh a sample of this base with any degree of accuracy. The first part of the experimental procedure involves the preparation of a solution of NaOH which is approximately 0.10 M, and the determination of the exact concentration by reaction with a known quantity of an acid, potassium hydrogen phthalate. This process of determining the exact concentration of a solution via a chemical reaction is called *standardization*. Once the exact concentration of NaOH is known, it will be reacted with a known mass of an unknown acid, and the equivalent weight of the acid determined.

The reaction of potassium hydrogen phthalate (KHP) with sodium hydroxide is:

$$KHC_8H_4O_{4(aq)} + NaOH_{(aq)} \rightarrow NaKC_8H_4O_{4(aq)} + H_2O_{(l)}$$

Several weighed portions of KHP will be dissolved in water and titrated with your sodium hydroxide solution to a phenolphthalein endpoint. Since the mass and the formula of KHP are known, the number of moles of protons donated is known. Each mole of protons (called an equivalent) requires a mole of hydroxide for neutralization. Using the number of moles of hydroxide needed for neutralization, and knowing the volume of NaOH dispensed from a buret to reach the endpoint, the concentration of NaOH can be calculated.

The second part of the experiment involves the same techniques of titration as the first, but now the exact concentration of the base is known. Several portions of an unknown acid will be weighed, dissolved in water, and titrated with your standardized NaOH solution to a phenolphthalein endpoint. The number of moles of hydroxide reacted is obtained from the concentration of NaOH (obtained from the first part of the experiment) and the volume of NaOH required for neutralization. The number of moles of protons reacted (called equivalents) equals the number of moles of hydroxide from the base solution. Using the mass of the sample and the number of equivalents of protons reacted, the equivalent weight of the acid can be calculated.

Proper laboratory technique is required in this procedure, and a large portion of your grade will depend on the accuracy and precision of your results.

II. Equipment Needed

This experiment requires the following:

- 50 mL graduated cylinder
- 500 mL storage bottle
- buret (from instructor)
- funnel
- ring stand and clamp
- small beaker
- 2 Erlenmeyer flasks
- glass stirring rod
- 600 mL beaker
- tripod or iron ring and wire gauze

III. Procedure

All glassware must be thoroughly cleaned and rinsed first with tap water and then distilled water. Your instructor will demonstrate the proper technique for cleaning and "lining" a buret. This technique is a way of rinsing a buret with a small amount of solution to minimize waste. Keep in mind that the sodium hydroxide solution which is prepared and standardized during the first week will be used again during the second week. Keep the cap on the storage bottle at all times to prevent changes in concentration.

A. Preparation and Standardization of NaOH

1. Using a stock solution of 1.0 M NaOH, prepare 500 mL of 0.10 M NaOH. Use the space below to calculate the volume of 1.0 M NaOH and the volume of distilled water to prepare the 500 mL of 0.10 M NaOH.

   Volume of 1.0 M NaOH:$(V_iM_i=V_fM_f)$

   Volume of distilled water:

   Graduated cylinders and volume markings on beakers are accurate enough. After thoroughly cleaning your storage bottle and rinsing with distilled water, transfer the NaOH solution to your bottle, cap it, and invert it several times to thoroughly mix the contents. **Label your bottle with your name, locker number and the date.**

2. Clean a buret with 5 mL of soap solution and a buret brush. Rinse the buret with small portions of tap water until there is no evidence of soap. Then rinse with three 5 mL portions of distilled water by "lining" the buret. Let some water flow through the tip of the buret.

3. Line the buret three times with 5 mL portions of your NaOH solution. Make sure some of the solution flows through the tip each time you line the buret. Using a funnel, fill the buret, including the tip, with your NaOH solution. You do not need to fill the buret to the zero line.

4. Place approximately 2.4 grams of potassium hydrogen phthalate (see the sample on the instructor's bench) in a small beaker and weigh the beaker and sample on the electronic analytical balance. (See operating instructions in the appendix of this manual.) Record the weight on the data sheet.

5. Transfer (without spilling) a sample with a mass of between 0.50 and 0.65 grams into one of your Erlenmeyer flasks. Label this flask sample #1. Reweigh the beaker and record the weight on the data sheet. Repeat this step of the procedure using a second Erlenmeyer flask. Label this flask sample #2. Be sure to reweigh the beaker and record the weight after the second sample has been removed.

6. Dissolve the KHP samples in 100 mL of distilled water and heat them to dissolve the sample and expel carbon dioxide which is absorbed from the air. Stir the

contents with a clean glass rod to help dissolve the KHP. Make sure to keep all of the sample within the flask by rinsing the stir rod into the flask before removing it. Once the solutions are warm and the sample has dissolved, cool the entire flask by immersing it in a large beaker containing cold tap water.

7. Remove the funnel from the top of the buret, and read and record the initial buret reading on the data sheet. The initial reading does not need to be at the zero line. Estimate to the nearest .01 mL by reading the bottom of the meniscus, being sure to read down from the top, rather than up from the bottom. (See Figure 19-1.)

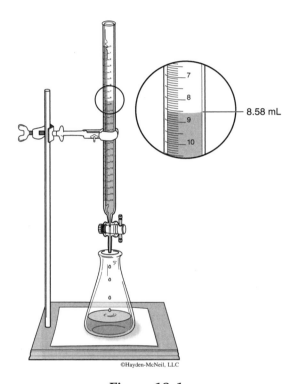

8.58 mL

©Hayden-McNeil, LLC

Figure 19-1.

8. Immediately after cooling the KHP solutions, add 3–4 drops of phenolphthalein indicator and titrate with NaOH until the first faint permanent pink color appears. A proper endpoint will be a very pale pink or pale orange color which persists for a minute. If the solution turns magenta, you have over-titrated and you should note this on your data sheet. Record the buret reading at the endpoint.

9. Refill the buret, take and record an initial buret reading, and titrate the second sample. Make sure you have added phenolphthalein to the flask (3–4 drops).

10. Prepare two more samples of KHP and titrate as described in steps 5–9.

11. Calculate the molarity of the NaOH solution for each titration. Your values should agree to within 0.0008 M. If you know a sample was over-titrated, you may discard it, but be sure to indicate this on your data sheet. If you do not have at least three values of molarity which agree within 0.0008 M, perform additional trials.

12. After performing all the calculations required for the report, transfer your results to the data sheet for the second half of this experiment.

13. When all trials have been completed, clean all glassware, label your storage bottle of NaOH with the average molarity, return any special equipment, and have your instructor sign your data sheet and lock your equipment drawer. Be sure to place your bottle of NaOH in your equipment drawer before leaving.

IV. Calculations

NOTE: This procedure can produce extremely accurate results. You will be graded on both your calculations and the accuracy of your results. Pay close attention to significant figures to receive proper credit for your work.

The calculations involved in determining the concentration of NaOH are relatively straightforward. For each sample of KHP titrated, you must first calculate the number of moles of KHP present. Using the complete formula of KHP, $KHC_8H_4O_4$, the molar mass can easily be calculated, as can the number of moles of acid present in the sample.

$$\text{moles } H^+ = \text{\# equivalents of acid} = \text{mass of KHP/molar mass KHP}$$

Since the reaction of KHP with NaOH is one-to-one, the number of moles of NaOH required for complete neutralization equals the number of moles of KHP titrated. Or, the number of equivalents of acid equals the number of equivalents of base. This statement is true for any acid–base neutralization regardless of the stoichiometry of the reaction. To calculate the concentration of the NaOH, divide the number of moles of NaOH by the volume of NaOH reacted (in liters).

$$M_{NaOH} = \text{moles NaOH/volume NaOH} = \text{equiv. KHP /volume NaOH}$$

You must calculate the number of equivalents of KHP and the molarity of NaOH separately for each trial. Once this has been done, calculate the average molarity of NaOH. You may discard a trial which is known to be in error due to over-titration, spilling of unknown, a leaky buret, etc. Note that you have discarded a trial on your report form, along with the reason for discarding the results. The deviation for each trial is calculated as follows:

$$\text{deviation} = \text{trial value} - \text{average value}$$

The average deviation is the sum of the absolute values of the deviation divided by the number of trials, and the percent deviation is calculated as follows.

$$\% \text{ deviation} = \frac{\text{average deviation}}{\text{average molarity}} \times 100\%$$

208

[Report Form]

Name	Section #

Instructor's Signature	Date

Standardization of NaOH

I. Data
Record data in ink with units.

A. Mass of KHP Samples

1. Mass of beaker + KHP   _____

2. Mass of beaker + KHP after 1st sample   _____

3. Mass of beaker + KHP after 2nd sample   _____

4. Mass of beaker + KHP after 3rd sample   _____

5. Mass of beaker + KHP after 4th sample   _____

6. Mass of beaker + KHP after 5th sample (if performed)   _____

B. Buret Readings

	Initial Reading	Endpoint Reading	Volume NaOH
Sample 1			
Sample 2			
Sample 3			
Sample 4			
Sample 5 (if performed)			

Notes: Indicate if a particular sample was over-titrated, lost due to spillage, etc.

II. Sample Calculations

A. **Mass of KHP, sample 1. Show the calculation, including units.**

B. **Moles KHP in sample 1. Show the calculations for the first trial.**

C. **Volume of NaOH in liters for trial 1. Show the calculation.**

D. **Molarity of NaOH from trial 1. Show the calculation, complete with units.**

III. Results

	Mass KHP	Moles KHP	V_{NaOH} (in liters)	M_{NaOH}
Trial 1				
Trial 2				
Trial 3				
Trial 4				
Trial 5 (if performed)				

[Report Form continued]

Name _____ Section # _____

A. Calculation of Average Molarity of NaOH

average M_{NaOH} = _____ *

B. Calculation of Deviation —Show calculation for trial #1.

Deviation Trial	#1	#2	#3	#4	#5
Results					

C. Average Deviation—Show Calculation

Average deviation in M_{NaOH} = _____ *

Note: Transfer the average molarity of NaOH and the average deviation in molarity of NaOH to the data sheet for next week's experiment and to the label on your storage bottle of sodium hydroxide.

D. **Percent Deviation—Show Calculations**

Percent deviation in M_{NaOH} = _____ *

IV. Questions

1. Why is it permissible to use graduated cylinders and the volume markings on beakers to prepare the .10 M NaOH solution?

2. Why will each student obtain a different molarity for the NaOH solution?

3. If you spill some of the potassium hydrogen phthalate while transferring it to the Erlenmeyer flask, how will it affect the calculated concentration of NaOH? Explain your answer.

III. Procedure (Week 2)

B. Determination of the Equivalent Weight of an Unknown Acid

The following equipment is needed:

- buret (from instructor)
- funnel
- ring stand and clamp
- small beaker
- 2 Erlenmeyer flasks
- glass stirring rod
- 600 mL beaker
- tripod or iron ring and wire gauze

1. Obtain a solid sample of an unknown acid from your laboratory instructor. Record the code number of the unknown on your data sheet.

2. Clean a buret with 5 mL of soap solution and a buret brush. Rinse the buret with small portions of tap water until there is no evidence of soap. Then rinse with three 5 mL portions of distilled water by "lining" the buret. Let some water flow through the tip of the buret.

3. Line the buret three times with 5 mL portions of your NaOH solution. Make sure some of the solution flows through the tip each time you line the buret. Using a funnel, fill the buret, including the tip, with your NaOH solution. You do not need to start at exactly zero.

4. Place your vial of unknown in a small clean dry beaker and weigh the beaker and vial on the electronic analytical balance. (See operating instructions in the appendix of this manual.) Record the weight on the data sheet.

5. Transfer (without spilling) a sample of your unknown with a mass of between 0.50 and 0.65 grams into one of your Erlenmeyer flasks. Label this flask sample #1. Reweigh the beaker and record the weight on the data sheet. Repeat this step of the procedure using a second Erlenmeyer flask. Label this flask sample #2. Be sure to reweigh the beaker and record the weight after the second sample has been removed.

6. Dissolve the unknown samples in 100 mL of distilled water and heat them to dissolve the sample and expel carbon dioxide which is absorbed from the air. Stir the contents with a clean glass rod to help dissolve the sample. Make sure to keep all of the sample within the flask by rinsing the stir rod into the flask before removing it. Once the solutions are warm and the sample has dissolved, cool the entire flask by immersing it in a large beaker containing cold tap water.

7. Remove the funnel from the top of the buret, and read and record the initial buret reading on the data sheet. Immediately after cooling the unknown solutions add 3–4 drops of phenolphthalein indicator and titrate with NaOH until the first faint permanent pink color appears. A proper endpoint will be a very pale pink or pale orange color which persists for a minute. If the solution turns magenta, you have over-titrated and you should note this on your data sheet. Record the buret reading at the endpoint.

8. Refill the buret, take and record an initial buret reading, and titrate the second sample. Make sure you have added phenolphthalein to the flask (3–4 drops).

9. Adjust your sample size so that 20–25 mL of NaOH will be required to reach the endpoint, and prepare two more samples as described in steps 5–6. Titrate as described in steps 7–8. If a sample is spilled or overtitrated and time permits, prepare a fifth sample and titrate.

V. Calculation of Equivalent Weight

The equivalent weight of the unknown acid is defined as the number of grams of acid which will provide one equivalent (one mole) of protons when reacted with a base. For each sample titrated:

$$\text{equivalent weight of the acid} = \frac{(\text{mass of a sample})}{(\text{\# moles of protons donated})}$$

$$= \frac{(\text{mass of a sample})}{(\text{moles NaOH reacted})} = \frac{(\text{mass of a sample})}{(M_{NaOH})(V_{NaOH^-}\text{ in liters})}$$

The average equivalent weight, deviation, and average deviation should be calculated as described in the previous section on the calculations for the molarity of the NaOH solution. The percent deviation in equivalent weight is calculated as follows:

$$\% \text{ deviation} = \frac{\text{average deviation}}{\text{average equiv. wt.}} \times 100\%$$

NOTE: Be sure to pay close attention to significant figures to receive proper credit for your work.

[Report Form]

Name	Section #

Instructor's Signature	Date

Equivalent Weight of an Unknown

I. Data
Record data in ink with units.

A. Average Molarity of NaOH (from previous week) _____

B. Unknown Acid Code # _____

C. Mass of Unknown Acid

    1. Mass of beaker + acid _____

    2. Mass of beaker + acid after 1st sample _____

    3. Mass of beaker + acid after 2nd sample _____

    4. Mass of beaker + acid after 3rd sample _____

    5. Mass of beaker + acid after 4th sample _____

    6. Mass of beaker + acid after 5th sample (if performed) _____

D. Buret Readings

	Initial Reading	Endpoint Reading	Volume NaOH
Sample 1			
Sample 2			
Sample 3			
Sample 4			
Sample 5 (if performed)			

Note: Indicate if a particular sample was over-titrated, lost due to spillage, etc.

II. Calculations

Show sample calculation, including any equations and units for sample #1.

A. Moles of NaOH Reacted with Sample #1

B. Mass of Unknown Acid Reacted, Sample #1

C. Equivalent Weight of Acid, Sample #1

D. Summary of Data and Results

	Moles NaOH Reacted	Mass of Acid	Equiv. wt. Acid
Sample 1			
Sample 2			
Sample 3:			
Sample 4			
Sample 5 (if performed)			

[Report Form]

Name _____ Section # _____

Instructor's Signature _____ Date _____

    E. Calculation of the Average Equivalent Weight

equiv. wt. = _____

    F. Calculation of Deviation—Show sample calculation for trial #1.

Deviation Trial	#1	#2	#3	#4	#5 (if performed)
Results					

    G. Average Deviation—Show calculation.

average deviation in equiv. wt. = _____

H. **Percent Deviation—Show calculation.**

percent deviation in equiv. wt. = _____

20 Experiment

Aqueous Acid–Base Equilibria and pH

I. Introduction

One of the most important properties of aqueous solutions is the concentration of hydronium ion present. The H_3O^+ ion (often written as H^+) greatly affects the solubility of many organic and inorganic substances, the nature of complex metal cations found in solution, and the rate of many chemical reactions, and it also may profoundly affect the reactions of biochemical species.

The pH Scale

Typically, the concentration of H_3O^+ ion in aqueous solutions may be small, requiring the use of scientific notation to describe the concentration numerically. For example, an acidic solution may have $[H_3O^+] = 2.3 \times 10^{-5}$ M, whereas a basic solution may have $[H_3O^+] = 4.1 \times 10^{-10}$ M. Because scientific notation may be difficult to deal with, especially when you make *comparisons* of numbers, a mathematical simplification, called pH, has been defined to describe the concentration of hydronium ion in aqueous solutions:

$$pH = -\log[H_3O^+]$$

By use of a base-10 logarithm, the power of ten of the scientific notation is converted to a "regular" number, and use of the minus sign in the definition of pH produces a positive value for the pH. For example, if $[H_3O^+] = 1.0 \times 10^{-4}$ M, then

$$pH = -\log[1.0 \times 10^{-4}] = -[-4.00] = 4.00$$

and similarly, if $[H_3O^+] = 5.0 \times 10^{-2}$ M, then

$$pH = -\log[5.0 \times 10^{-2}] = -[-1.30] = 1.30$$

Although basic solutions are usually considered to be solutions of *hydroxide* ion, OH^-, basic solutions also must contain a certain concentration of *hydronium* ion, H_3O^+, because of the equilibrium that exists in aqueous solutions as a consequence of the autoionization of water. The concentration of hydronium ion in a basic solution can be determined by reference to the equilibrium constant for the autoionization of water, K_w:

$$K_w: = [H_3O^+] [OH^-] = 1.0 \times 10^{-14} \text{ (at 25°C)}$$

For example, if a basic solution contains $[OH^-]$ at the level of 2.0×10^{-3} M, then the solution also contains hydronium ion at the level of:

$$[H^+] = 1.0 \times 10^{-14}/[OH^-]$$

$$[H^+] = 1.0 \times 10^{-14}/[2.0 \times 10^{-3}] = 5.0 \times 10^{-12} \text{ M}$$

In pure water, there must be equal concentrations of hydronium ion and hydroxide ion (one of each ion is produced when a water molecule ionizes). Hence, in pure water:

$$[H_3O^+] = [OH^-] = (1.0 \times 10^{-14})^{1/2} = 1.0 \times 10^{-7} \text{ M}$$

The pH of pure water is thus 7.00; this value serves as the *dividing line* for the pH of aqueous solutions. A solution in which there is *more* hydronium ion than hydroxide ion ($[H_3O^+] > 1.0 \times 10^{-7}$ M) will be *acidic* and will have pH less than 7.00. Conversely, a solution with *more* hydroxide ion than hydronium ion ($[OH^-] > 1.0 \times 10{-7}$ M) will be *basic* and will have pH greater than 7.00.

If the pH of a solution is known (or has been measured experimentally), then the hydronium ion concentration of the solution may be calculated:

$$[H_3O^+] = 10^{-pH}$$

For example, the hydronium ion concentration of a solution with pH = 4.20 would be given by

$$[H_3O^+] = 10^{-pH} = 10^{-4.20} = 6.3 \times 10^{-5} \text{ M}$$

Note that every place after the decimal in a pH value results in a significant digit in $[H_3O^+]$.

Experimental Determination of pH

The experimental determination of the pH of a solution is commonly performed by either of two methods. The first of these methods involves the use of chemical dyes called **indicators**. These substances are generally weak acids or bases and can exist in either of two colored forms, depending on whether the molecule is protonated or has been deprotonated. For example, let HIn represent the protonated form of the indicator. In aqueous solution, an equilibrium exists:

$$HIn \rightleftharpoons H^+ + In^-$$
$$\textit{first} \qquad \textit{second}$$
$$\textit{color} \qquad \textit{color}$$

Depending on what other acidic/basic substances are present in the solution, the equilibrium of the indicator will shift, and one colored form of the indicator will predominate over the other and impart its color to the entire solution.

The pH of a solution may also be determined using a pH meter. This is an electronic device, which uses an electrode capable of detecting H_3O^+ ion.

Strong and Weak Acids/Bases

Some acids and bases undergo substantial ionization when dissolved in water and are called **strong acids** or **strong bases**. Strong acids and bases are *completely* ionized in dilute aqueous solutions. Other acids and bases, because they ionize *incompletely* in water (often to the extent of only a few percent), are called **weak acids** or **weak bases**. Hydrochloric acid (HCl) and sodium hydroxide (NaOH) are a typical strong acid and a typical strong base, respectively. A 0.1 M solution of HCl contains hydronium ion at effectively 0.1 M concentration because of the complete ionization of HCl molecules.

$$HCl_{(aq)} \rightarrow H^+_{(aq)} + Cl^-_{(aq)}$$
$$0.1 \text{ M} \qquad 0.1 \text{ M} \qquad 0.1 \text{ M}$$

Similarly, a 1×10^{-2} M solution of NaOH contains hydroxide ion at the level of 1×10^{-2} M concentration because of the complete ionization of NaOH.

$$NaOH_{(aq)} \rightarrow Na^+_{(aq)} + OH^-_{(aq)}$$
$$1 \times 10^{-2} \text{ M} \qquad 1 \times 10^{-2} \text{ M} \qquad 1 \times 10^{-2} \text{ M}$$

Acetic acid ($HC_2H_3O_2$ or CH_3COOH) and ammonia (NH_3) are typical examples of a weak acid and a weak base, respectively. Weak acids and weak bases must be treated by the techniques of chemical equilibrium in determining the concentrations of hydronium ion or hydroxide ion in their solutions. For example, for the general weak acid HA, the equilibrium reaction would be

$$HA_{(aq)} \rightleftharpoons H^+_{(aq)} + A^-_{(aq)}$$

or

$$HA_{(aq)} + H_2O_{(l)} \rightleftharpoons H_3O^+_{(aq)} + A^-_{(aq)}$$

and the equilibrium constant expression would be given by

$$K_a = \frac{[H^+][A^-]}{[HA]}$$

For acetic acid, as an example, the ionization equilibrium reaction and K_a are represented by the following:

$$CH_3COOH_{(aq)} \rightleftharpoons H^+_{(aq)} + CH_3COO^-_{(aq)}$$

$$K_a = \frac{[H^+][CH_3COO^-]}{[CH_3COOH]}$$

K_a is a constant and is characteristic of the acid HA. For a given weak acid, the product of the concentrations in the expression will remain constant at equilibrium, regardless of the manner in which the solution of the acid was prepared. For a general weak base B, the equilibrium reaction would be

$$B_{(aq)} + H_2O_{(l)} \rightleftharpoons BH^+_{(aq)} + OH^-_{(aq)}$$

and the equilibrium constant expression would be given by

$$K_b = \frac{[BH^+][OH^-]}{[B]}$$

As an example, the ionization and K_b for the weak base ammonia are represented by

$$NH_{3(aq)} + H_2O_{(l)} \rightleftharpoons NH_4^+_{(aq)} + OH^-_{(aq)}$$

$$K_b = \frac{[NH_4^+][OH^-]}{[NH_3]}$$

pH of Salt Solutions

Salts that can be considered to have been formed from the complete neutralization of strong acids with strong bases—such as NaCl (which can be considered to have been produced by the neutralization of HCl with NaOH)—ionize completely in solution. Such strong acid/strong base salts do not react with water molecules to any appreciable degree (do not undergo hydrolysis) when they are dissolved in water. Solutions of such salts are neutral and have pH = 7. Other examples of such salts are KBr (from HBr and KOH) and $NaNO_3$ (from HNO_3 and NaOH).

However, when salts formed by the neutralization of a *weak* acid or base are dissolved in water, these salts furnish ions that tend to react to some extent with water, producing molecules of the weak acid or base and releasing some H_3O^+ or OH^- ion to the solution. Solutions of such salts will *not* be neutral but, rather, will be acidic or basic themselves.

Consider the weak acid HA. If the sodium salt of this acid, Na^+A^-, is dissolved in water, the A^- ions released to the solution will react with water molecules to some extent.

$$A^-_{(aq)} + H_2O_{(aq)} \rightleftharpoons HA_{(aq)} + OH^-_{(aq)}$$

The solution of the salt will be *basic* because hydroxide ion has been released by the reaction of the A^- ions with water. For example, a solution of sodium acetate (a salt of the weak acid acetic acid) is basic because of reaction of the acetate ions with water molecules to form hydroxide ions:

$$CH_3COO^-_{(aq)} + H_2O_{(l)} \rightleftharpoons CH_3COOH_{(aq)} + OH^-_{(aq)}$$

Conversely, solutions of salts of weak bases (such as $NH_4^+Cl^-$, derived from the weak base NH_3) will be *acidic*, because of reaction of the ions of the salt with water. For example,

$$NH_4^+_{(aq)} + H_2O_{(l)} \rightleftharpoons NH_{3(aq)} + H_3O^+_{(aq)}$$

Many salts of transition metal ions are acidic. A solution of $Cu(NO_3)_2$ or $FeCl_3$ will typically be of pH 5 or lower. The salts are completely ionized in solution. The acidity comes from the fact that the metal cation is hydrated. For example, $Cu(H_2O)_4^{2+}$ better represents the state of a copper(II) ion in aqueous solution. The large positive charge on the metal cation attracts electrons from the O–H bonds in the water molecules, thereby weakening the bonds and producing some H^+ ions in the solution:

$$Cu(H_2O)_4^{2+}_{(aq)} \rightleftharpoons Cu(H_2O)_3(OH)^+_{(aq)} + H^+_{(aq)}$$

Buffered Solutions

Some solutions, called buffered solutions or "buffers," are remarkably resistant to pH changes caused by the addition of an acid or base from an outside source. A **buffered solution** in general is a mixture of a weak acid and a weak base. The most common sort of buffered solution consists of a mixture of a conjugate acid–base pair. For example, a mixture of the *salt of a weak acid or base* and the *weak acid or base itself* would constitute a buffered solution.

If a small amount of strong acid were added to the buffered system from an external source, the H_3O^+ ion introduced by the strong acid would tend to react with the basic A^- ion of the salt, thereby preventing a change in pH. Similarly, if a strong base were added to the HA/A⁻ system from an external source, the OH^- introduced by the strong base would tend to be neutralized by the HA present in the buffered system. If similar small amounts of strong acid or strong base were added to a non-buffered system (such as plain distilled water), the pH would be changed drastically.

For example, consider a buffer containing 0.1 mol of acetic acid, $HC_2H_3O_2$ and 0.1 mol of sodium acetate, $Na^+C_2H_3O_2^-$. If a few drops of hydrochloric acid (a strong acid) were added to this mixture, the additional hydrogen ion would be consumed by reaction with the acetate ion: (The Na^+ is just a spectator ion, and does not react.)

$$H^+ \text{ (from HCl)} + C_2H_3O_2^- \text{(from buffer)} \rightarrow HC_2H_3O_2$$

The relative amounts of acetic acid and sodium acetate would be changed, and the pH of the solution would decrease slightly, but not nearly to the same extent as if an equivalent amount of HCl had been added to an unbuffered system such as plain water. Suppose, instead, a few drops of sodium hydroxide (a strong base) had been added to the buffer. The additional hydroxide ion would be consumed by reaction with the acetic acid of the buffer:

$$OH^- \text{ (from NaOH)} + HC_2H_3O_2 \text{ (from buffer)} \rightarrow H_2O + C_2H_3O_2^-$$

Again, the relative amounts of acetic acid and sodium acetate would be changed, and the pH of the solution would increase slightly, but not nearly to the same extent as if an equivalent amount of NaOH had been added to an unbuffered system such as plain water.

The ability of a buffer to neutralize strong acids or bases is finite, however. The buffer consumes added acid or base by reacting with it, and once one of the components of the buffer is exhausted, the solution will no longer resist changes in its pH. The extent to which a buffer can counteract the influence of strong acids or strong bases is referred to as the *buffer capacity* of the buffer system and depends on the concentrations of the components of the buffer.

SAFETY PRECAUTIONS:

- **Wear safety glasses at all times while you are in the laboratory, whether or not you are working on the experiment.**

- **Assume that all solutions are corrosive and damaging to skin, eyes, and clothing. Wash if spilled. Clean up all spills on the benchtop.**

II. Equipment Needed

This experiment requires the following:

- 24-well plate

- several strips of pH test paper

- glass stir rod

- several droppers

- several small (75 mm × 10 mm) test tubes

III. Procedure

A. pH of Strong and Weak Acids/Bases

1. Place 10 drops of the following solutions into separate wells of your 24-well plate: 0.1 M HCl, 0.1 M $HC_2H_3O_2$, 0.1 M NaOH, and 0.1 M NH_3.

2. Use a separate strip of pH test paper to determine the pH of each of the solutions. All four colored spots on the pH paper must be wetted and must be matched to the color chart.

3. Explain why the pH of the $HC_2H_3O_2$ solution is higher than the pH of the HCl solution, although both solutions are at the same molar concentration, 0.1 M.

4. Explain why the pH of the NH_3 solution is lower than the pH of the NaOH solution, although both solutions are at the same molar concentration, 0.1 M.

5. Using your approximate pH values for the $HC_2H_3O_2$ and NH_3 solutions, and the fact that the solutions taken were 0.1 M in those substances, calculate approximate values for K_a for $HC_2H_3O_2$ and for K_b for NH_3.

B. pH of Salt Solutions

Salts are ionic compounds that may have acidic or basic properties. If the negative ion of the salt is the conjugate base of a weak acid, then the salt will be basic in solution. The negative ion gains hydrogen ions from water to form the weak acid, leaving an excess of hydroxide ion in the solution. If the positive ion of the salt is the conjugate acid of a weak base, then the salt will be acidic in solution. The positive ion loses hydrogen ions to water to form the weak base.

1. Place 10 drops of the following salt solutions into separate wells of your 24-well plate: 0.1 M NaCl, 0.1 M $NaC_2H_3O_2$, 0.1 M Na_2CO_3, and 0.1 M NH_4Cl.

2. Add 1 drop of Universal Indicator to each sample in the 24-well plate, and record the approximate pH of each sample using the color chart provided with the indicator.

3. For each salt, explain the observed pH of the solution, using a chemical equation to demonstrate why some salts are expected to be basic and some acidic.

C. Titrations of Strong Acid/Strong Base and Weak Acid/ Strong Base

The titration of a strong acid with a strong base differs from the titration of a weak acid with a strong base. When a weak acid is reacted with a strong base, a *buffered system* begins to form. The formation of a buffered system means that the changes in pH become much more gradual for the weak acid/strong base titration as additional strong base is added.

1. Place 10 drops of 0.1 M HCl into a small test tube. Add one drop of Universal Indicator and record the approximate pH of the solution using the color chart provided with the indicator.

2. Add one drop of 0.1 M NaOH to the HCl sample, tap the test tube to mix, and record the pH.

3. Continue adding 0.1 M NaOH to the HCl one drop at a time, recording the approximate pH of the sample after each drop has been added until you have added a total of 25 drops of NaOH.

4. Repeat the process, using 0.1 M $HC_2H_3O_2$ in place of the 0.1 M HCl.

5. Prepare a graph of "pH" (y-axis) versus "number of drops of NaOH added" (x-axis) for the HCl and $HC_2H_3O_2$ samples. Explain the differences in the two graphs.

D. Buffered Solutions

Although any buffer solution will resist changes in its pH when strong acids or bases are added to it, the *extent* to which strong acids or bases can be counteracted depends on the *concentrations* of the components of the buffer. This is described as the buffer *capacity* of the buffer solution.

1. Prepare an acetic acid/sodium acetate buffer solution by combining 10 drops of 0.1 M $HC_2H_3O_2$ solution and 10 drops of 0.1 M $NaC_2H_3O_2$ solution in a small test tube.

2. Prepare a second buffer solution of acetic acid/sodium acetate in a different small test tube, only this time use only *one* drop of each component, plus 18 drops of water.

3. In a third small test tube, place 20 drops of water to serve as a control (an unbuffered sample).

4. Add 1 drop of Universal Indicator to each of the three samples and record the approximate pH using the color chart provided with the indicator.

5. Add 0.1 M NaOH one drop at a time to each of the three samples, and count the total number of drops of NaOH required to raise the pH of each sample to above pH 10.

[Report Form]

Name	Section #

Instructor's Signature	Date

I. Data, Explanations, and Calculations

A. pH of Strong and Weak Acids

Sample	pH Observed
0.1 M HCl	
0.1 M $HC_2H_3O_2$	
0.1 M NaOH	
0.1 M NH_3	

Explanation of relative pHs of HCl and $HC_2H_3O_2$:

_____

_____

_____

Explanation of relative pHs of NaOH and NH_3:

_____

_____

_____

Calculation of approximate K_a for $HC_2H_3O_2$:

Calculation of approximate K_b for NH_3:

B. pH of Salt Solutions

Salt	pH	Equation Explaining Observed pH of Salt Solution
NaCl		
$NaC_2H_3O_2$		
Na_2CO_3		
NH_4Cl		

C. Titrations of Strong Acid/Strong Base and Weak Acid/Strong Base

HCl/NaOH

Drops NaOH	pH	Drops NaOH	pH	Drops NaOH	pH	Drops NaOH	pH
1		7		13		19	
2		8		14		20	
3		9		15		21	
4		10		16		22	
5		11		17		23	
6		12		18		24	

$HC_2H_3O_2$/NaOH

Drops NaOH	pH	Drops NaOH	pH	Drops NaOH	pH	Drops NaOH	pH
1		7		13		19	
2		8		14		20	
3		9		15		21	
4		10		16		22	
5		11		17		23	
6		12		18		24	

[Report Form continued]

Name   Section #

Graphs: Plot your data for both HCl and $HC_2H_3O_2$ on the same graph, using differ-ent color inks to distinguish the graphs (indicate which is which). The graph is *not* expected to be a straight line, so draw the smoothest curve possible between your data points. Since the data is only approximate, the graph paper below is acceptable.

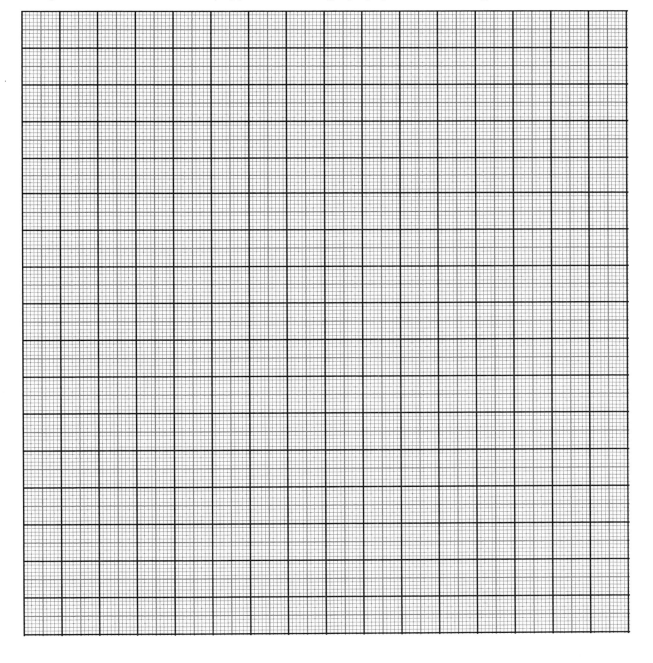

Explain the differences between the two graphs.

_____

_____

_____

D. Buffered Solutions

Sample	# Drops NaOH to Reach pH 10
10 drops $HC_2H_3O_2$/10 drops $NaC_2H_3O_2$	
1 drop $HC_2H_3O_2$/1 drop $NaC_2H_3O_2$/18 drops water	
Water	

Explain your results in terms of the buffer capacity of each of the three samples.

_____

_____

_____

_____

_____

II. QUESTIONS

Benzoic acid, C_6H_5COOH, is a weak acid with $K_a = 6.3 \times 10^{-5}$.

$$C_6H_5CO_2H_{(aq)} + H_2O_{(l)} \rightleftharpoons H_3O^+_{(aq)} + C_6H_5CO_2^-_{(aq)}$$

1. Calculate the pH of a 0.150 M benzoic acid solution. Show all calculations.

[Report Form continued]

2. Suppose 1.44 g of sodium benzoate, $Na^+C_6H_5COO^-$, is added to 100.0 mL of the 0.150 M benzoic acid solution. Calculate the pH of the resulting buffer solution assuming the volume of the solution does not change on addition of the solid.

232

21 Experiment

Electrochemical Cells

I. Introduction

Several electrochemical cells will be constructed and their potential measured using a voltmeter. Calculations of equilibrium constants and free energy changes will be made using the measured cell potentials. (See your textbook for a detailed explanation of electrochemical cells.) You will also observe demonstrations of electrolysis reactions.

Most cells to be constructed will be under nonstandard conditions in which the concentration of reagents may not be 1.00 M, and the temperature may not be exactly 298K (25°C).

Electrochemical cells are constructed by connecting two half-cells so as to make a complete circuit. Consider the following two half-reactions:

$$Cu^{2+}_{(aq)} + 2e^- \rightarrow Cu^0_{(s)} \qquad E^\circ = +0.34 \text{ volts}$$

$$Zn^{2+}_{(aq)} + 2e^- \rightarrow Zn^0_{(s)} \qquad E^\circ = -0.76 \text{ volts}$$

In order for the above reactions to produce a measurable electrical potential, a redox reaction with a positive cell potential must be possible. Since both reactions are written as reductions, one must be reversed, as reduction is not possible unless oxidation takes place as well. Reversing the reduction of zinc ion gives:

$$Zn^0_{(s)} \rightarrow Zn^{2+}_{(aq)} + 2e^- \qquad E^\circ = +0.76 \text{ volts}$$

Combining this reaction with the reduction of copper(II) ion gives a redox reaction with a positive cell potential.

reduction:	$Cu^{2+} + 2e^- \rightarrow Cu^0$	$E^\circ = +0.34$ volts
oxidation	$Zn^0 \rightarrow Zn^{2+} + 2e^-$	$E^\circ = +0.76$ volts
	$Zn^0 + Cu^{2+} \rightarrow Zn^{2+} + Cu^0$	$E^\circ = +1.10$ volts

The above reaction is the only oxidation–reduction reaction which will give a positive cell potential. The anode is the electrode at which oxidation takes place, and will be made of Zn metal. The cathode, the site of reduction, will be made of Cu metal. The cell can be written in a shorthand notation as follows:

$$Zn|Zn^{2+} \ (1 \ M)| \ |Cu^{2+} \ (1 \ M)|Cu$$

The anode is always written on the left side, and the cathode on the right side. The single vertical lines represent the boundary between a solution and the solid electrode, and the double vertical lines represent a physical barrier between the two half-cells.

In order to construct an electrochemical cell which produces electricity, all four components of the above reaction must be present, and the half-reactions must be physically separate from each other. That is, if zinc metal is immersed in a solution of copper(II) ion, the reaction will occur, but there is no way to measure the flow of electrons from zinc to the cupric ion. The cell is usually constructed with the zinc metal and zinc ion solution in one beaker, and copper metal and cupric ion solution in another beaker. These beakers are called half-cells. The two half-cells must be connected in a complete circuit before electrons can flow from zinc to Cu^{2+} ion and the cell potential measured. A typical setup is illustrated below.

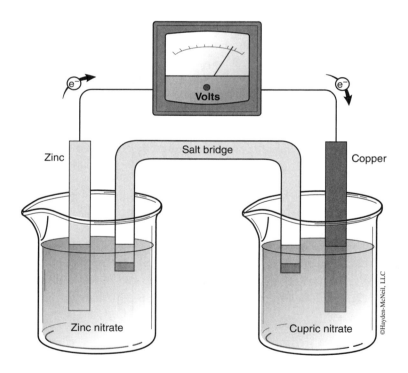

Figure 21-1. Half-cell setup.

Electrons can flow through the wire and voltmeter from the zinc metal to the Cu^{2+} ions only if a salt bridge completes the circuit. The salt bridge is usually a glass tube containing a gel of KNO_3 or another salt. It permits the flow of current by keeping the total charge in each beaker neutral. In the beaker on the left, zinc metal is entering solution and leaving two electrons to flow through the wire. The Zn^{2+} ion cannot enter the solution unless there are two anions to neutralize its charge. The salt bridge provides two NO_3^- ions for every Zn^{2+} ion which is formed. Likewise, Cu^{2+} ion is picking up the two electrons and leaving the solution on the right by plating out on the piece of copper metal. Two nitrate ions are left behind in solution for every two electrons transferred along the wire. The salt bridge prevents a buildup of negative charge in the beaker on the right by releasing two K^+ ions for every Cu^{2+} ion which leaves solution.

Under ideal standard conditions, this cell should have a potential of 1.10 volts at the beginning of the reaction. As the reaction progresses, several changes can be observed. The intensity of the blue color of the $Cu(NO_3)_2$ solution will fade as cupric ion leaves solution. The copper metal will increase in size and mass as copper plates out, the zinc metal will decrease in size and mass as it dissolves, and the concentration of zinc ion will increase. The measured cell potential will gradually decrease as the reaction progresses. The Nernst equation can be used to calculate the potential for the above cell under nonstandard conditions.

$$E_{cell} = E^\circ - \frac{2.303RT}{nF} \log \frac{[Zn^{2+}]}{[Cu^{2+}]}$$

where R = the gas constant, 8.314 J/K-mol
T = temperature in degrees Kelvin
n = # moles of electrons transferred
F = Faraday's constant, 96500 J/V-mol

The Nernst equation shows that as the reaction progresses and the zinc ion concentration increases and the copper(II) ion concentration decreases, the negative term will get larger. Eventually, the system will reach equilibrium, and the cell potential will be zero. For this reason, it is important to make measurements as soon as the cell has been constructed, and not to let the reaction proceed for any length of time.

The Nernst equation shows that cells can produce electrical current when they are not at equilibrium. An interesting application of this phenomenon is a **concentration cell**. A concentration cell contains two half-cells with the same material for the anode and cathode, and the same metal ions in solution, only differing in concentration. For example, a concentration cell could be made with 1.0 M $Cu(NO_3)_2$ and a copper strip in one half-cell, and 0.01 M $Cu(NO_3)_2$ and a copper strip in the other half-cell. Clearly, if the two solutions were placed in the same beaker they would mix until an equilibrium concentration of cupric nitrate was reached. Since the two solutions are physically separated, electrons are transferred from the less concentrated one (as Cu metal dissolves to enter solution) to the more concentrated one (as Cu^{2+} takes on electrons and plates out on the electrode) until the concentration of Cu^{2+} ion is the same in both half-cells. (Calculation of the cell potential using the Nernst equation can be found in your textbook.)

In this experiment you will create a concentration cell using 0.10 M Cu^{2+} in one half-cell. The other half-cell will also contain 0.10 M Cu^{2+} to which NaOH has been added. The hydroxide ion reacts with the copper ion to produce a precipitate of $Cu(OH)_2$

As a result, the Cu^{2+} concentration in solution is very small. The difference in concentration of Cu^{2+} in each half-cell results in the production of a voltage.

You will be constructing electrochemical cells using a porous cup instead of a salt bridge, with sulfate salts rather than nitrate salts. The apparatus is illustrated below. One electrode and solution is in a beaker. The other half-cell consists of a metal strip and a solution in a porous cup. The porcelain cup is placed inside the beaker as illustrated. The cup will permit the anions (as well as the metal ions) to pass through it. In this way the two solutions will remain neutral in charge. (See Figure 21-2.)

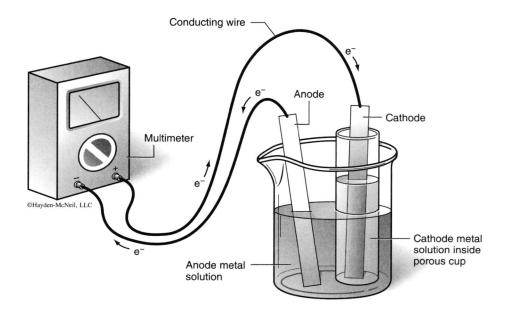

Figure 21-2. Voltmeter.

II. Equipment Needed

This experiment requires the following:

- porous cup and electrodes (from instructor)
- 200 mL beaker
- tongs
- wash bottle
- several 100 mL beakers
- thermometer (from instructor)

III. Procedure

A. Observations of Electrolysis Reactions

The pre-lab video shows an electrolysis reaction. It will be the electrolysis of aqueous potassium iodide containing some phenolphthalein. Record your observations on the laboratory report form.

B. Observation of a Redox Reaction

1. Obtain a porous cup and set of electrodes from your instructor. There should be electrodes made of Cu(2), Zn, Mg, and Fe.

2. The porous cup and the copper, zinc, and iron electrodes should be cleaned by dipping in nitric acid cleaning solution prior to each use. **Do not clean the Mg electrode.**

    Using a 400 mL beaker, obtain 200 mL of nitric acid cleaning solution. **CAUTION:** Nitric acid is caustic. Rinse all spills immediately with lots of tap water and sodium bicarbonate solution.

    Soak the porous cup and dip the electrodes in the acid solution before use. Use tongs to remove the cup and electrodes from the cleaning solution, and rinse all items with distilled water before proceeding.

3. Solutions of 0.10 M $CuSO_4$, $ZnSO_4$, $MgSO_4$, and $FeSO_4$ are available in the laboratory. A total of six different electrochemical cells can be constructed using these solutions and the metal electrodes. Before constructing the electrochemical cells, you will observe the spontaneous redox reaction between zinc and copper.

4. Place approximately 20 mL of 0.10 M $ZnSO_4$ solution in a 100 mL beaker, and place approximately 20 mL of 0.10 M $CuSO_4$ solution in another 100 mL beaker. Observe the color of the solutions and record your observations.

5. Place a clean Cu electrode in the zinc sulfate solution, and place a clean Zn electrode in the copper(II) sulfate solution. Wait 5 minutes and record your observations. Is there any sign that a reaction occurred? The redox reaction that occurs spontaneously will be the same reaction that occurs in the electrochemical cell. Since the reactants in an electrochemical cell are not in physical contact, the electron transfer occurs through the wire, producing a measurable voltage.

C. Construction of Electrochemical Cells

1. Discard the copper(II) sulfate solution in the waste container. Clean the Cu and Zn electrodes as described in Part B, step 2, and construct a half-cell by placing the clean Zn electrode in the beaker containing 20 mL of 0.10 M $ZnSO_4$ solution.

2. Construct the other half-cell by placing 12 mL of 0.10 M $CuSO_4$ in the porous cup along with the clean copper strip.

3. Do not place the porous cup in the beaker until you are ready to make a measurement. Bring the two half-cells to the voltmeter. (See operating instructions after Part C of the procedure.) Connect the leads to the voltmeter, adjust the range switch to the proper setting, and then place the porous cup in the beaker. Do not leave the voltmeter connected longer than is necessary. Record the highest potential reached on the display, disconnect the meter, and remove the porous cup from the beaker. Keep the half-cell in the porous cup intact, and retain the zinc sulfate solution for further measurements.

4. Keep the $Cu/CuSO_4$ half-cell in the porous cup and construct a $Fe/FeSO_4$ half-cell, using 20 mL of iron(II) sulfate solution, in a 100 mL beaker. Connect the half-cells to the voltmeter as described above in step 3. Record the highest potential reached, remove the porous cup from the beaker, and retain the iron(II) sulfate solution and the $Cu/CuSO_4$ half-cell for further measurements.

5. Using the $Cu/CuSO_4$ half-cell in the porous cup, construct a $Mg/MgSO_4$ half-cell in a 100 mL beaker and measure and record the highest potential reached as described in step 3. Transfer the copper(II) sulfate solution to a beaker for later use, and place the porous cup in the cleaning solution. Rinse the cup with distilled water prior to use.

6. Take the $Mg/MgSO_4$ half-cell in the beaker from step 5, and combine it with a half-cell made from 12 mL of the previously used $ZnSO_4$ solution placed in the cleaned porous cup. Place the zinc strip in the porous cup and bring both half-cells to the voltmeter. Connect the electrodes to the meter and combine the cells as described in step 3.

7. Replace the contents of the beaker with an $Fe/FeSO_4$ half-cell, leaving the porous cup half-cell intact, and measure and record the potential as in step 3. Discard the zinc sulfate solution which is in the porous cup and soak the cup in the cleaning solution. Rinse the cup with distilled water prior to use.

8. Take the $Fe/FeSO_4$ half-cell in the beaker from step 7, and combine it with a half-cell consisting of the previously used $MgSO_4$ solution and the magnesium strip in the porous cup. Measure and record the cell potential as in step 3. Discard both solutions and soak the porous cup in the cleaning solution. Rinse the cup with distilled water prior to use.

D. The Copper(II) Ion Concentration Cell

1. You should have a beaker with 10–12 mL of copper(II) sulfate in it. This will go back into the porous cup with the (cleaned) copper strip.

2. Clean a second copper strip in the nitric acid cleaning solution.

3. Take 10 mL of fresh 0.10 M $CuSO_4$ solution and place it in a 100 mL beaker. Add 2.0 mL of 1.0 M NaOH to the beaker and stir to ensure complete precipitation of $Cu(OH)_2$.

4. Allow the precipitate to settle, place the copper strip in the beaker, and construct a cell with the $Cu/CuSO_4$ half-cell in the porous cup. Measure and record the maximum potential as described in step 3, Part C.

5. Obtain a thermometer and record the temperature of the solution in the beaker.

6. Discard all solutions and soak the porous cup in the cleaning solution for several minutes before removing it. Rinse it thoroughly with distilled water and dry it under a heat lamp.

7. Rinse all metal strips, dry them, and return them and the dry porous cup to your instructor. Have your instructor sign your data sheet and lock your equipment drawer before leaving.

OPERATION OF VOLTMETERS
1. The voltmeter should be plugged in and turned on 1/2 hour before use. The switches on the top row of the instrument should be set for DC Voltage. If not, press the "V" and "DC,Ω" buttons.

2. There should be two wire leads attached to the voltmeter. Before placing the porous cup in the beaker, attach the leads. The black lead should be attached to the anode (listed on the left in the cell notation) and the red lead should be attached to the cathode (on the right in the cell notation).

3. Press the appropriate voltage range. (You can estimate the cell potential by using the standard cell potentials in the introduction and the equation: $E^o_{cell} = E^o_{cathode} - E^o_{anode}$.) In most cases the 20V range will be adequate. If the voltage is out of range, "error" will appear on the display. Change the range until a voltage reading can be obtained.

4. After setting the appropriate voltage range, place the porous cup in the beaker and record the highest voltage reached. Do not leave the porous cup in the beaker for extended periods of time.

5. Remove the porous cup from the beaker and disconnect the wire leads from the metal electrodes.

IV. Calculations

A. Observation of Electrolysis Reaction
The electrolysis of aqueous KI with phenolphthalein was shown on the introductory video for the experiment. Below are listed all of the possible reactions (written as reductions) which might have occurred in each cell. Choose the pair of oxidation and reduction reactions that are consistent with your observations. Indicate the reactions at the anode and the cathode on your report form. The lecture course textbook provides a more detailed discussion of electrolysis.

Electrolysis of KI: Possible Reactions (written as reductions, reverse the direction of the reaction for an oxidation)

$$K^+_{(aq)} + e^- \rightarrow K_{(s)} \qquad\qquad -2.93V$$

$$2H_2O_{(l)} + 2e^- \rightarrow H_{2(g)} + 2\,OH^-_{(aq)} \qquad -0.83V$$

$$I_{2(s)} + 2e^- \rightarrow 2I^-_{(aq)} \qquad\qquad +0.53V$$

$$O_{2(g)} + 4\,H^+_{(aq)} + 4e^- \rightarrow 2\,H_2O_{(l)} \qquad +1.23V$$

$$H_2O_{2(aq)} + 2\,H^+ + 2e^- \rightarrow 2\,H_2O_{(l)} \qquad +1.77V$$

B. Observation of an Oxidation–Reduction Reaction

You should have observed signs of a reaction (change in the color of the solution, formation of metal crystals, etc.) in one of the beakers. The reaction that occurs is an electron transfer from the metal strip to the ions in solution. You will write the balanced chemical reaction on your lab report form. Keep in mind that the number of electrons lost must equal the number of electrons gained.

C. Construction of Electrochemical Cells

The standard reduction potentials for all half-cells used in this experiment are listed below.

Half-reaction	E^o (Volts)
$Mg^{2+}_{(aq)} + 2e^- \rightarrow Mg_{(s)}$	-2.37
$Zn^{2+}_{(aq)} + 2e^- \rightarrow Zn_{(s)}$	-0.76
$Fe^{2+}_{(aq)} + 2e^- \rightarrow Fe_{(s)}$	-0.44
$Cu^{2+}_{(aq)} + 2e^- \rightarrow Cu_{(s)}$	$+0.34$
$Fe^{3+}_{(aq)} + 1e^- \rightarrow Fe^{2+}_{(aq)}$	$+0.77$

For each electrochemical cell constructed you will be required to calculate the standard cell potential and compare it to the measured cell potential. Since all of the cells constructed in Part C of the procedure have equal concentrations of both metal ions, and room temperature is close to 25°C, the measured cell potential should be approximately equal to the standard cell potential. The standard cell potential is the sum of the standard potentials of each half-reaction (see the example in the introduction).

Measured cell potentials often are not the same as the standard calculated cell potentials due to changes in concentration as the reaction progresses, resistance of flow of electrons through the wire and voltmeter, and resistance of flow of ions through the porous cup. Calculate the % difference (not strictly a % error, as there are practical reasons why the theoretical and actual cell potentials differ) between the experimental cell potential and the standard cell potential as follows:

$$\% \text{ difference} = \frac{E_{measured} - E^o_{theoretical}}{E^o_{theoretical}} \times 100\%$$

The standard Gibbs free-energy change, $\Delta G°$, can be calculated for each cell using the equation,

$$\Delta G = -nFE$$

D. The Copper(II) Ion Concentration Cell

An electrochemical cell is constructed using 0.10 M $CuSO_4$ and copper electrodes in both half-cells. The addition of NaOH to one half-cell causes most of the copper(II) ion to precipitate out of solution as $Cu(OH)_2$. The difference in concentration of copper(II) ion in the two half-cells causes a voltage to be produced. The Nernst equation can be used to calculate the concentration of Cu^{2+} in equilibrium with $Cu(OH)_2$ as follows. The electrons will flow from the less concentrated half-cell (the one containing solid cupric hydroxide) to the half-cell with 0.10 M cupric ion until the concentrations of Cu^{2+} are equal in both halves of the cell. The half-reactions are:

in $Cu(OH)_2$ half-cell:	$Cu_{(s)} \rightarrow Cu^{2+}_{(aq)} + 2e^-$	(oxidation)
in 0.10 M Cu^{2+} half-cell:	$Cu^{2+}_{(ag)} + 2e^- \rightarrow Cu_{(s)}$	(reduction)
overall reaction:	Cu^{2+} (0.10 M) $\rightarrow Cu^{2+}$ (? M)	

The concentration of cupric ion on the right side is the $[Cu^{2+}]$ which is in equilibrium with solid $Cu(OH)_2$, and is what we wish to determine. Applying the Nernst equation to this cell we obtain:

$$E_{cell} = E° - \frac{2.303RT}{nF} \log \left([Cu^{2+}]_{eq} / 0.10 \right)$$

$E°$ for the cell will be zero since $E°_{cathode} = E°_{anode}$, so the equation simplifies to:

$$E_{cell} = \frac{-2.303RT}{nF} \left(\log[Cu^{2+}]_{eq} - \log 0.10 \right)$$

where E_{cell} = measured potential

      R   = 8.314 J/K-mol

      T   = temperature in degrees Kelvin

      n   = # moles of e^- = 2

      F   = 96,500 J/V-mol

The equation can be rearranged to solve for $\log [Cu^{2+}]_{eq}$, and the antilog taken to give the value of $[Cu^{2+}]_{eq}$.

242

[Report Form]

Name   Section #

Instructor's Signature   Date

I. Data

A. Observation of Electrolysis Reaction

Electrolysis of KI (with phenolphthalein). Describe your observations at each electrode. Note color changes, evolution of gas, etc.

B. Observation of a Redox Reaction

1. $ZnSO_4$ solution and Cu electrode:
   Initial appearance of solution and electrode:

   Appearance after 5 minutes:

2. $CuSO_4$ solution and zinc electrode:
   Initial appearance of solution and electrode:

   Appearance after 5 minutes:

C. Electrochemical Cells. Below is the notation for each cell to be constructed. Record the highest potential reached for each cell.

1. $Zn|Zn^{2+}(0.10\ M)|\ |Cu^{2+}(0.10\ M)|Cu$ $E_{maximum}$ _____

2. $Fe|Fe^{2+}(0.10\ M)|\ |Cu^{2+}(0.10\ M)|Cu$ $E_{maximum}$ _____

3. $Mg|Mg^{2+}(0.10\ M)|\ |Cu^{2+}(0.10\ M)|Cu$ $E_{maximum}$ _____

4. $Mg|Mg^{2+}(0.10\ M)|\ |Zn^{2+}(0.10\ M)|Zn$ $E_{maximum}$ _____

5. $Zn|Zn^{2+}(0.10 \text{ M})|\ |Fe^{2+}(0.10 \text{ M})|Fe$ $E_{maximum}$ _____

6. $Mg|Mg^{2+}(0.10 \text{ M})|\ |Fe^{2+}(0.10 \text{ M})|Fe$ $E_{maximum}$ _____

D. The Copper(II) Ion Concentration Cell

1. $E_{maximum}$ of cell = _____

2. Temperature of the solution = _____

II. Calculations and Conclusions

A. Electrolysis Reactions

1. Electrolysis of KI. Using the possible reactions listed in the *Calculations* section of this experiment and your observations, determine the reaction at the anode and the reaction at the cathode. Clearly explain how your observations are consistent with the products formed at each electrode.

    Anode reaction:

    Cathode reaction:

    Explanation of observations:

B. Oxidation–Reduction Reaction.
Based on your observations of the mixtures of Cu with zinc(II) ion and Zn with copper(II) ion, write the balanced reaction that occurred spontaneously.

C. Electrochemical Cells.
Write the half-reactions and overall reaction for each cell, and compare the experimental potential to the standard cell potential. Show your work, including all units, etc.

1. $Zn|Zn^{2+}(0.10 \text{ M})|\ |Cu^{2+}(0.10 \text{ M})|Cu$

    Reaction at anode:

    Reaction at cathode:

[Report Form continued]

Name   Section #

Overall reaction:

Standard E° (using table) = _____. The % difference = _____.
(show calculation)

2. $Fe|Fe^{2+}(0.10 M)| |Cu^{2+}(0.10 M)|Cu$

   Reaction at anode:

   Reaction at cathode:

   Overall reaction:

   Standard E° (using table) = _____. The % difference = _____.
   (show calculation)

   Note that the list of reduction reactions includes the reduction of iron(II) to elemental iron, and also the reduction of iron(III) to iron(II). Is your data more consistent with the formation of Fe^{2+} or Fe^{3+}? Explain your answer.

3. $Mg|Mg^{2+}(0.10 M)| |Cu^{2+}(0.10 M)|Cu$

   Reaction at anode:

Reaction at cathode:

Overall reaction:

Standard $E°$ (using table) = _____. The % difference = _____.
(show calculation)

4. $Mg|Mg^{2+}(0.10\ M)|\ |Zn^{2+}(0.10\ M)|Zn$

Reaction at anode:

Reaction at cathode:

Overall reaction:

Standard $E°$ (using table) = _____. The % difference = _____.
(show calculation)

5. $Zn|Zn^{2+}(0.10\ M)|\ |Fe^{2+}(0.10\ M)|Fe$

Reaction at anode:

Reaction at cathode:

Overall reaction:

[Report Form continued]

Standard E^o (using table) = _____. The % difference = _____.
(show calculation)

6. $Mg|Mg^{2+}(0.10\ M)|\ |Fe^{2+}(0.10\ M)|Fe$

Reaction at anode:

Reaction at cathode:

Overall reaction:

Standard E^o (using table) = _____. The % difference = _____.
(show calculation)

D. The Copper(II) Ion Concentration Cell

1. Calculation of $[Cu^{2+}]_{eq}$ using measured cell potential and the Nernst equation.

III. Questions

1. All of the electrodes except Mg are cleaned using nitric acid. Why does the procedure instruct you to not clean the Mg electrode? Be specific.

2. The value of ΔH for the concentration cell [the one with saturated $Cu(OH)_2$] is zero (since the overall reaction simply represents the mixing of the same solution at different concentrations), yet the cell produces an electrical potential. What is the driving force of the "reaction"?

3. Use the measured potential of your concentration cell to calculate ΔG_{mixing}. Show your work, including any formulas used.

4. Use your calculated value of ΔG_{mixing} and the temperature of the solutions to calculate the entropy of mixing under your experimental conditions. Clearly show all your work.

22 | Experiment

Determination of Calcium in Antacids: A Complexation Titration

I. Introduction

Calcium, often in the form of calcium carbonate, is added to various foods such as soft drinks and orange juice to help prevent osteoporosis, a condition in which bone degenerates as a person ages. Since older people often don't drink or can't metabolize milk products, many products are currently being formulated with extra calcium. Many antacid tablets are now being made with calcium carbonate rather than sodium bicarbonate to both decrease the amount of sodium ion (which has been linked to high blood pressure), and to provide a source of calcium. In this experiment, you will determine, via titration, the amount of calcium in a commercially available antacid.

The basis for the titration is a complexation reaction. In such a reaction a metal ion is reacted with a molecule or ion which donates electrons to the metal. The resulting complex ion is often extremely stable. In this titration, calcium ion will be reacted with a large organic ion called ethylenediamine tetraacetate. The ion, drawn below, is usually referred to as EDTA.

Figure 22-1. Ethylenediamine tetraacetate (EDTA).

In basic solutions, four acidic hydrogens (attached to oxygens on the COO^- groups) can ionize to produce the above acetate ion with a -4 charge. This ion reacts with Ca^{2+} and many other metal ions to form a complex ion in which the EDTA ion surrounds the metal and is attached to it in several places. The metal ion has six sites, located at the corners of an octahedron, at which the EDTA can be attached. The four oxygen atoms (negatively charged since the hydrogen ion is removed in base) and the two nitrogen atoms become attached to the calcium ion to produce a complex ion with the structure shown below.

The stoichiometry of the reaction is 1:1 and can be represented by the chemical equation:

$$Ca^{2+}_{(aq)} + EDTA^{4-}_{(aq)} \rightleftharpoons [Ca(EDTA)]^{2-}_{(aq)}$$

The indicator for the titration involves a competing complexation reaction. The indicator contains a mixture of eriochrome black T, a colored organic compound which can react with metal ions and hydronium ions, and Mg^{2+} ion. At the proper pH (above 10), the indicator will exist as a Mg-eriochrome black T complex ion. The formula of this complex will be simplified as $[Mg\text{-}In]^-$. The color of the magnesium-indicator complex ion is red. The complex will react with protonated EDTA to produce the protonated indicator in the form HIn^{2-} which is blue in color.

$$MgIn^-_{(aq)} + HEDTA^{3-}_{(aq)} \rightleftharpoons MgEDTA^{2-}_{(aq)} + HIn^{2-}_{(aq)}$$
$$\quad\text{red}\qquad\qquad\qquad\qquad\qquad\qquad\qquad\qquad\text{blue}$$

The indicator stays in the red form as calcium ion in the sample is reacting with the EDTA. When virtually all of the calcium ion has complexed with the EDTA, additional EDTA reacts with the Mg-indicator complex ion and the color changes from red to blue. For accurate results, the pH and the amount of indicator added to each sample must be precisely controlled.

II. Equipment Needed

This experiment requires the following:

- 250 mL volumetric flask and buret (from instructor)
- 25 mL pipet and rubber bulb (from instructor)
- 50 mL and 10 mL graduated cylinders
- 2 – 100 mL plastic beakers
- 400 mL beaker
- funnel
- wash bottle
- eyedropper
- Erlenmeyer flasks
- several small beakers
- plastic storage bottle

III. Procedure

1. Clean a buret, a 250 mL volumetric flask, and a plastic storage bottle first with soap and water, and then rinse with tap water followed by distilled water. If properly cleaned, the buret will drain without leaving drops of water on the inner walls.

2. Weigh a clean dry plastic 100 mL beaker on the electronic analytical balance and record the weight. Add a 1.9 gram sample of $Na_2EDTA \cdot 2H_2O$ to the beaker and obtain the mass (to four decimal places) on an analytical balance. The sample need not weigh exactly 1.9 grams, but you must know and record the exact weight of the sample.

3. Obtain 300 mL of distilled water in a clean beaker. Add some distilled water to the EDTA sample, and quantitatively transfer **all** of the sample to the volumetric flask using a funnel. Rinse the beaker, using a wash bottle, into the funnel, and then rinse the funnel, with all rinsings going into the volumetric flask. When the flask is approximately 1/2 full, swirl the contents until mixed.

4. After mixing, add water from a beaker to the flask until the level reaches the base of the neck of the flask. Fill a clean eyedropper with distilled water and slowly add water until the bottom of the water line is even with the fill line on the neck of the flask.

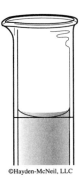

©Hayden-McNeil, LLC

Figure 22-2. For a glass flask, fill with distilled water until the meniscus is on the fill line.

If you have a plastic flask, the water line will appear flat, and should be just at the line on the neck of the flask. If your volumetric flask is made of glass, the bottom of the curved surface of the water (called the meniscus) should be sitting on the line on the neck of the flask.

5. Cap the volumetric flask and invert it several times to thoroughly mix the contents. After mixing, rinse the storage bottle with several small (5–10 mL) samples of the EDTA solution, by swirling the portions of solution so that they have contact with all the inner surfaces of the bottle. Discard rinsings in the sink, and fill the bottle with the remaining solution. Calculate the molarity of the solution, and label the bottle with your name, the concentration and formula of the contents, and the date.

6. Rinse the volumetric flask with several portions of distilled water. Discard the rinsings in the sink.

7. Weigh a clean dry plastic 100 mL beaker on the electronic analytical balance (see operating instructions in the appendix), and record the weight on the data sheet. Place an antacid tablet in the beaker, reweigh, and record the weight on the data sheet. Also record the brand of antacid and the mg calcium listed on the label.

8. Dissolve the tablet in approximately 10 mL of 6 M HCl. Some of the binders in the tablet may not dissolve. If the solution is cloudy or contains some particles but no longer bubbles when HCl is added, proceed. **CAUTION:** Hydrochloric acid is highly caustic. Wash all spills with sodium bicarbonate solution and lots of water. Report all spills to your instructor.

9. Quantitatively transfer the acid solution containing the tablet to a 250 mL volumetric flask, using a funnel. Make sure all of the solution goes into the flask by rinsing the beaker and funnel with a wash bottle containing distilled water. Make sure all washings go into the flask.

10. Fill the flask (using a beaker of distilled water) and mix the contents as described previously. Keep the flask capped when not in use.

11. Clean a 25 mL pipet until water drains from it without clinging to the inner walls. Place approximately 15 mL of the antacid tablet solution in a small beaker, and draw up small portions of this solution into the pipet using a rubber bulb. With 2–3 mL in the pipet, remove the bulb, cover the tip with your finger, and tilt the pipet to coat the walls. Discard rinsings down the sink. After three rinsings, using a fresh portion of the antacid solution, fill the pipet by squeezing the bulb, placing the bulb over the top opening of the pipet, and releasing the bulb. **Do not let the solution go into the bulb.** Once the liquid level is near the top volume markings on the pipet, remove the bulb and cover the top opening with your index finger. You can gently release the pressure of your finger to release liquid from the pipet. Pipet a 25 mL sample into a clean 250 mL Erlenmeyer flask. **Do not** blow out the small amount of liquid which remains in the tip of the pipet.

12. Rinse the buret with your EDTA solution by lining the buret with three 5 mL portions of the solution. Be sure to rinse the tip, and discard all rinsings in the sink. Using a funnel, fill the buret with your EDTA solution. Remove the funnel and record the initial buret reading by reading the level of the meniscus to the nearest 0.01 mL. You do not need to start on the zero line as long as you record the initial level.

13. Add 50 mL of distilled water and approximately 10 mL of pH 10 NH_3/NH_4^+ buffer to the Erlenmeyer flask using a graduated cylinder. **CAUTION:** The buffer contains concentrated ammonia. Add it to the sample **under the hood**.

    Add 5 drops of eriochrome black T indicator. The sample should be wine-red in color.

14. Titrate the antacid sample in the Erlenmeyer flask by adding the EDTA solution. The endpoint is reached when the red color disappears. The solution may turn gray (due to the presence of both the blue and red forms of the indicator) very close to the endpoint. Record the buret reading at the endpoint.

15. Pipet another 25 mL sample of antacid solution into a 250 mL Erlenmeyer flask and treat the sample according to the procedure in steps 13–14. Refill the buret and record the initial reading at the beginning of each titration. Repeat until a total of four trials have been performed.

16. Since the sample size for each titration is the same, the volume of EDTA required for each sample should be the same. Compare your results for each trial. If there is poor agreement (deviations of >.08 mL from the average volume required) and time permits, perform additional trials.

17. Clean all glassware and discard the EDTA and antacid solutions in the sink, followed by lots of water. Return the pipet and bulb to your instructor, and have your data sheet signed and equipment drawer locked before leaving the laboratory.

IV. Calculations

Since the stoichiometry of the reaction between EDTA and Ca^{2+} is 1:1, one mole of calcium ion is present for every mole of EDTA needed to reach the endpoint. However, since the antacid sample was not a solution, but a tablet, and since most products are labeled in milligrams calcium rather than moles, some conversion of units will be required.

To calculate the concentration of the EDTA solution, determine the number of moles of $Na_2EDTA \cdot 2\ H_2O$ (molar mass of 372.24 grams/mole) which were dissolved to make exactly 250 mL of solution. The 250 mL volumetric flask is accurate to four significant figures, or .2500 liters. Pay close attention to significant figures, as virtually all quantities are known to 4 or 5 significant figures.

At the endpoint, the moles EDTA = moles Ca^{2+}. This equation can be put in the more useful form:

$$\left(V_{EDTA}\right)\left(M_{EDTA}\right) = \text{moles } Ca^{2+} = \frac{\left(\text{grams } Ca^{2+}\right)}{\left(\text{atomic mass of Ca}\right)}$$

where V_{EDTA} is the volume of EDTA in liters
M_{EDTA} is the molarity of EDTA

The above equation can be rearranged to calculate the number of grams of calcium in each 25.00 mL portion of the antacid solution. To determine the number of milligrams of calcium in the **entire** sample, the following calculation must be performed.

$$\text{mg Ca per tablet} = \frac{\left(\text{grams Ca}\right)}{\left(25.00\ \text{mL soln}\right)} \frac{\left(10^3\ \text{mg}\right)}{\left(\text{grams}\right)} \frac{\left(250.0\ \text{mL soln}\right)}{\left(\text{tablet}\right)}$$

The number of mg of calcium per tablet should be calculated for each trial and then averaged. The deviation is calculated by subtracting each trial value from the average value. The average deviation is the sum of the absolute values of the deviation divided by the number of trials.

[Report Form]

Name	Section #

Instructor's Signature	Date

I. Data

Record data in ink with units.

A. Mass of EDTA

1. Mass of empty beaker   _____

2. Mass of beaker $+$ $Na_2EDTA \cdot 2\ H_2O$ _____

3. Mass of $Na_2EDTA \cdot 2\ H_2O$ _____

B. Antacid Data

1. Mass of antacid tablet   _____

2. Brand of antacid tablet   _____

3. mg calcium stated on label of antacid   _____

C. Buret Readings and V_{EDTA}

	Initial Reading	Final Reading	V_{EDTA}
Trial 1			
Trial 2			
Trial 3			
Trial 4			

Include any comments on the titrations, including whether the sample was over-titrated, spilled during pipetting, etc.

II. Calculations

Show a sample calculation, where requested, complete with formulas (if any), units, and the method of calculation. Pay close attention to significant figures.

A. Molarity of EDTA Solution

$$M_{EDTA} = \underline{\hspace{3cm}}$$

B. **Grams of Ca in Sample 1**

grams Ca = _____

C. **Milligrams Ca in Tablet Based on Trial 1**

mg Ca = _____

III. Results

	mg Ca in Tablet	Deviation
Trial 1		
Trial 2		
Trial 3		
Trial 4		
Average		

Average mg Ca in tablet—show calculation, and write result in table above.

average mg Ca = _____

[Report Form continued]

Average deviation in mg Ca in tablet—show calculation and write result in table above.

average deviation = _____

Compare your average value to the mg Ca stated on the label of the antacid. Assuming that the value on the label is the correct value, calculate the % error in your results.

$$\% \ error = \frac{experimental \ value - correct \ value}{correct \ value} \times 100\%$$

258

23 Experiment

The Microscale Synthesis of Soap

I. Introduction

Commercial soaps have a dual chemical nature which is related to their function of cleaning. Most stains and spots on clothing are due to organic materials such as oils, grease, and foods. Soaps need to contain an organic fragment to dissolve these stains. However, since clothes are washed in water, soaps must also be water soluble so that the soap can be easily rinsed from the cloth. Structurally, in order to accomplish both tasks, soaps generally consist of a salt (usually of sodium or potassium) of a long organic acid (called a **fatty acid**). The long carbon chain is effective in dissolving oils and grease, and the ionic nature of the soap allows it to be water soluble.

The synthesis of soap has been performed for centuries, and historically involved rendering (heating or melting) fats with wood ashes (which are basic), or with lye (potassium or sodium hydroxide). Although it may seem strange to use fat to make soap, the fat serves to provide the long organic chain needed to produce an effective ("fat-dissolving") soap. The strong base serves to break the fat molecules into shorter chains which are ionic.

Oils and fats have the general formula given below. They consist of **triesters** (molecules with three ester linkages) made from fatty acids combined with a three-carbon alcohol called **glycerol** (see formula on the following page). The R group of the ester typically contains 15–20 carbon atoms depending on the source of the fat or oil.

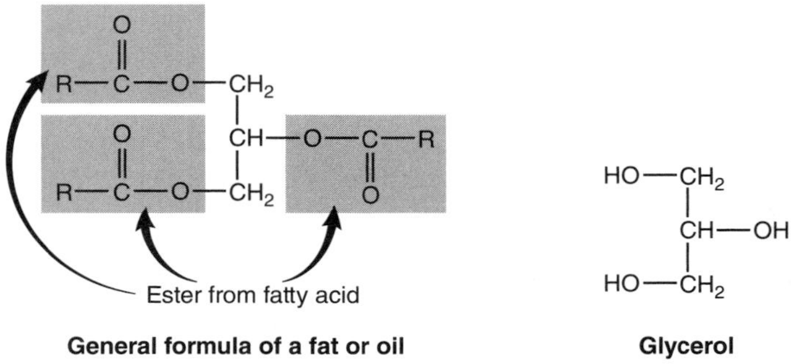

Figure 23-1.

The fat or oil can be broken down into glycerol and soap via hydrolysis with strong base. Reaction with sodium hydroxide will break the bonds between the esters and the three-carbon chain connecting them and produce three moles of soap (the sodium salt) and a mole of glycerol.

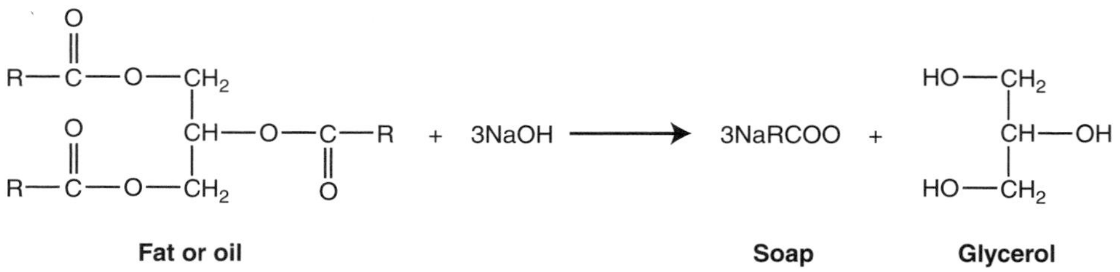

Figure 23-2.

In this experiment you will prepare soap in microscale, using a micropipet as the reaction vessel, and study its properties compared to those of commercial soaps and detergents.

II. Equipment Needed

This experiment requires the following:

- Bunsen burner and striker
- tripod or ring stand and ring
- wire gauze
- 150 mL glass beaker
- thermometer (from instructor)
- 2 watch glasses
- plastic micropipet
- several small beakers

- spoon

- Kimwipes

- 50 mL graduated cylinder

- 250 mL Erlenmeyer flask

- several small test tubes

- test tube rack

- several medium-sized test tubes

III. Procedure

1. Set up a bunsen burner, wire gauze, and tripod (or ring stand and iron ring), and heat 100 mL of water in a 150 mL glass beaker to a temperature of 70–90°C. **CAUTION:** Keep the lighted flame away from ethanol, as ethanol is an extremely flammable solvent.

2. In a small plastic beaker combine 15 drops of cottonseed oil, 8–10 drops of ethanol, and 7–8 drops of 30% NaOH solution. **CAUTION:** NaOH is caustic and damages tissue and can cause severe burns. Wear proper eye protection at all times and wash your hands, any glassware, and the benchtop after using the solution.

3. Cut the tip of a plastic micropipet until it is approximately 1 inch in length. Squeeze the bulb and suck the mixture in the beaker into the pipet.

4. Invert the pipet in a small beaker and let it stand for approximately 5 minutes. After this time the mixture should separate into two layers. The top layer should be colorless (NaOH and ethanol) and the bottom layer yellow (oil).

5. Place the inverted pipet into the beaker of heated water. Maintain a temperature of approximately 80°C by intermittent heating. Carefully shake the pipet periodically to mix the reactants, and to see if the mixture is homogenous (no longer contains two layers). Proceed once the mixture contains only one layer.

6. Remove the pipet from the hot water and place it (still inverted) in a small empty beaker to cool. Obtain approximately 20 mL of saturated NaCl solution in a small beaker.

7. When the liquid in the micropipet has cooled to room temperature, squirt the contents into the beaker containing the NaCl solution.

   Draw up several portions of the salt solution into the pipet to rinse any soap out of the pipet and into the beaker of saturated NaCl. Flakes of soap should float on the surface of the salt solution. **NOTE:** The NaCl solution helps separate the soap from solution. This process is called "salting out" the soap.

8. Skim off the flakes of soap with a spoon, and dry them on a Kimwipe or a piece of filter paper which has been placed on a watch glass. Pat the soap with the paper to remove as much water as possible.

9. Describe the appearance of the soap on your laboratory report form. Dissolve the entire sample in 50 mL of distilled water in a 250 mL Erlenmeyer flask. Shake the flask vigorously and note if a lather develops. This soap solution will be used for the tests described in the next section.

The Properties of Soaps—Discussion and Tests

A. Basic Properties

The general formula for soap shows that soaps are the salts of long chain organic acids. Since these acids come from fats and oils, they are commonly called **fatty acids**. Salts of weak acids should undergo hydrolysis and be basic in water.

1. Transfer 5 mL of your soap solution to a test tube and add 1 drop of Universal Indicator. Compare the color of the indicator with the key, and determine the pH of your soap solution. Record both the color and corresponding pH on your data sheet. Repeat this test with samples of commercial soaps and detergents which are in the laboratory.

B. Reactions with Metal Ions

Sodium and potassium salts of fatty acids are soluble in water, whereas salts of fatty acids containing most other metal ions are insoluble. When someone says they have "hard water," it's because soap tends to precipitate out of water and form a grey ring on the sides of the bathtub. The reason for this is that hard water often contains Ca^{2+} ions. Calcium ions are often present in well water and water from rivers and lakes due to the leaching of limestone ($CaCO_3$).

Commercial (synthetic) detergents are designed to overcome some of the deficiencies of natural soaps. Although chemically similar, they generally will not precipitate out when in the presence of hard water (calcium, magnesium, or iron(III) ions).

1. Place 5 mL samples of your soap and each of the commercial soaps into separate test tubes. Add 1% $CaCl_2$ dropwise to each sample until a total of approximately 1 mL of the calcium chloride has been added to each test tube. Which samples produce a precipitate? What does the precipitate look like? Record your observations on the data sheet.

2. Repeat the procedure in step 2 using a 1% solution of $FeCl_3$ instead of calcium chloride. Record which soaps produce a precipitate and the appearance of the solid formed on your data sheet.

C. Emulsifying Properties

Soaps can dissolve well in both water and oils. They can thus serve as *emulsifying* agents. That is, they allow oil and water to mix. In this section you will examine the emulsifying ability of your soap and those which are commercially available.

1. Place 10 mL of each soap sample into separate test tubes. Also place 10 mL of distilled water into a test tube. Add 10 drops of cottonseed oil to each test tube and shake the contents of each test tube thoroughly. Immediately after shaking, note the extent to which the contents of each test tube have mixed together uniformly (emulsified). Record your observations on the data sheet.

2. Allow the test tubes from step 1 to sit undisturbed in a rack for 5 minutes. Record the extent to which the oil remains mixed in suspension in each test tube. If it helps, you can draw the appearance of the contents of each test tube on the data sheet.

D. Reaction with Acid

The soap you synthesized is the salt of a weak organic acid called a fatty acid. In this last test you will observe the effect of adding acid to your soap solution.

1. Swirl the remaining soap solution until it froths. Record the appearance of the solution.

2. Add 3–4 mL of 1 M HCl to the soap solution and swirl the flask again. Record your observations.

264

[Report Form]

Name   Section #

Instructor's Signature   Date

I. Data
Record data in ink.

A. Describe the appearance of your soap product.

B. Universal Indicator Test

Soap Solution Tested	Color of Indicator	pH of Solution

C. Water Hardness Tests. Record your observations below.

Soap Solution Tested	With 5% $CaCl_2$	With 5% $FeCl_3$

D. Emulsification of Oil. Record your observations (both immediately after shaking and after waiting 5 minutes) for your soap, commercial soaps, and distilled water.

Solution Tested	Appearance After Shaking	After 5 Minutes

E. Addition of HCl to Soap

    a.   Appearance of swirled soap solution before addition of HCl.

    b.   Appearance of soap solution after addition of HCl.

    c.   Using Na^+RCOO^- as the general formula of soap, write the reaction of soap with HCl.

    d.   Does the flask still contain soap after the addition of HCl? Explain your answer.

24 Experiment

Determination of the Length of Stearic Acid

I. Introduction

The object of this experiment is to determine the length of an organic molecule, stearic acid. Stearic acid is a long-chain hydrocarbon with a polar carboxyl group (–COOH) on one end.

The hydrocarbon chain is nonpolar, and considered *hydrophobic*. It is not attracted to polar molecules like water. The carboxyl group is polar, and contains a C–O–H bond, which enables the polar end to be attracted to water, and hence *hydrophilic*.

Hydrophobic tail

Hydrophilic head

Stearic acid, when added to water, tends to form a *monolayer* that is a single molecule thick. The thickness of the monolayer represents the approximate length of the stearic acid molecules. In this experiment you will create a monolayer of stearic acid using a known volume of the acid. By measuring the area of the monolayer, you will use your data to estimate the length of the stearic acid molecule.

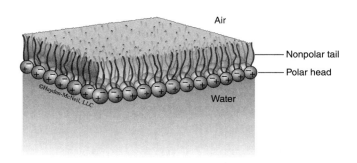

Figure 24-1. The stearic acid monolayer.

II. Equipment

This experiment requires the following:

- 9-inch aluminum or plastic plate or pan

- long-tip glass Pasteur pipets and bulb

- lycopodium powder or powdered sulfur

- stearic acid solution in cyclohexane (0.15 g stearic acid/L of solution)

- 10 mL graduated cylinder

- small beaker and watch glass cover

- wash bottle with distilled water

- see-through plastic ruler

SAFETY PRECAUTIONS
- **Stearic acid and the lycopodium powder are both highly flammable. No flames are permitted in the laboratory.**

- **The stearic acid solution should be kept in the fume hood during the experiment.**

III. Procedure

A. Calibration of the Pipet

1. Obtain a Pasteur pipet (glass with a long thin tip) and bulb. You will need to calibrate the pipet and bulb to determine the volume of each drop.

2. Take a small clean beaker and a watch glass to the hood containing the stearic acid solution. Place approximately 5 mL of the stearic acid solution in the beaker, cover it with the watch glass, and place it under the hood at your laboratory bench.

3. Transfer approximately 3 mL of the stearic acid solution into a 10 mL graduated cylinder and record the volume. Be sure to estimate one place beyond the smallest division on the graduated cylinder.

4. Using your Pasteur pipet, count the number of droplets as you transfer exactly 1 mL of the stearic acid solution from the beaker to the graduated cylinder. Record the number of droplets on the data sheet.

5. Calculate the volume of a single droplet of the stearic acid solution and record the value on the data sheet.

6. Pour the contents of the graduated cylinder back into the beaker, and repeat steps 3–5. Average your two values for the volume of a single droplet and record it on the data sheet.

B. Preparation of the Monolayer

1. Obtain an aluminum or plastic plate or pan and a see-through plastic ruler.

2. Clean the plate or pan with soap and water, and rinse under the tap for at least two minutes to remove all traces of soap. Rinse with several portions of distilled water from your wash bottle. It is essential that the plate or pan be clean of all oils (including oils from your skin) and soap so that the monolayer can properly form.

3. Place the plate or pan on a clean flat surface under the fume hood and add distilled water to a depth of approximately ½ an inch.

4. Lycopodium powder (or powdered sulfur) is used to make the monolayer more visible. Lycopodium powder is a finely divided moss which will float on the surface of the water. Obtain a small amount of lycopodium powder (or sulfur) and spread it out thinly on a small sheet of paper. From about a foot away, using a short sharp puff of air, blow the powder onto the surface of the water. If done correctly, the powder will evenly cover the surface of the water in the pan without clumping.

5. Fill your calibrated pipet with the stearic acid solution. Position the tip of the pipet approximately 1 cm above the surface of the water in the pan, at the *center of the pan*. Carefully add 10–12 drops (count them exactly) of the stearic acid solution to the center of the water in the pan. Record the number of drops. The solution may initially bead up on the surface of the water. As the cyclohexane solvent evaporates, the monolayer will form. Watch the surface carefully. As the monolayer forms, it will push the powder outward, forming a ring.

6. Quickly measure and record the diameter of the monolayer using the see-through ruler. If the monolayer isn't circular, measure the diameter at several places. Record the values, and use the average for your calculations.

7. Thoroughly clean out the plate or pan, and repeat steps 2–6 two more times for a total of three trials. For each trial, be sure to record the exact number of droplets of stearic acid solution used, and the diameter of the monolayer that forms.

8. Return the plate or pan to your instructor, and have your instructor sign your report form and lock your equipment drawer before leaving the laboratory.

IV. Calculations

Using the diameter of the monolayer in each trial, calculate the area of the circular layer.

$$\text{area of circle} = \pi r^2 = \pi(\text{diameter}/2)^2$$

The stearic acid solution contains 0.15 grams of stearic acid per liter of solution. Using the volume of each droplet that was obtained when you calibrated the pipet, you can calculate the mass of stearic acid in the monolayer.

$$(\text{\# of drops})(\text{mL/drop})\ (1\ \text{liter}/1000\ \text{mL})\ (0.15\ \text{g stearic acid/liter}) = \text{mass of stearic acid}$$

The density of pure stearic acid is 0.848 g/mL. Using the mass of stearic acid in the monolayer and the density, you can calculate the volume of pure stearic acid in each of the monolayers.

$$\frac{\text{mass of stearic acid}}{\text{density of stearic acid}} = \text{volume of stearic acid}$$

The volume of the monolayer equals the area × height. Using the area of each monolayer and the volume of stearic acid in each layer, you can calculate the thickness of each layer. This will be the approximate length of the stearic acid molecule.

$$\frac{(\text{volume of stearic acid})}{(\text{area of monolayer})} = \text{length of stearic acid}$$

[Report Form]

Name   Section #

Instructor's Signature   Date

Determination of the Length of Stearic Acid

I. Data
Record data in ink, with units.

A. **Calibration of the Pipet**	**Trial 1**	**Trial 2**
1. Graduated Cylinder:		
Initial Volume	_____	_____
Final Volume	_____	_____
Volume of Stearic Acid	_____	_____
Number of Drops	_____	_____

2. Calculation of Volume of a Drop—Show Calculation for Trial 1

3. Results: Volume of a drop	_____	_____
4. Average volume of a drop	_____	

B. **Measurements of Monolayer**	**Trial 1**	**Trial 2**	**Trial 3**
1. Number of drops in monolayer	_____	_____	_____
2. Diameter of monolayer	_____	_____	_____
Additional values if not round	_____	_____	_____
Additional values if not round	_____	_____	_____
Average diameter of monolayer	_____	_____	_____

II. Calculations and Results

Show a sample calculation, complete with equations, units, and the correct number of significant figures for trial 1.

A. Area of monolayer (show calculation for trial 1)

Results: Trial 1: _____   Trial 2: _____   Trial 3: _____

B. Mass of stearic acid in monolayer (show calculation for trial 1)

Results: Trial 1: _____   Trial 2: _____   Trial 3: _____

C. Volume of stearic acid in monolayer (show calculation for trial 1)

Results: Trial 1: _____   Trial 2: _____   Trial 3: _____

D. Thickness of monolayer (show calculation for trial 1)

Results: Trial 1: _____   Trial 2: _____   Trial 3: _____

III. Final Results

A. Length of Stearic Acid Molecule

Results: Trial 1: _____   Trial 2: _____   Trial 3: _____

B. Average Length of Stearic Acid Molecule: _____

IV. Questions

1. Hydrocarbons typically have a carbon-to-carbon bond length of 1.54 Angstroms. An Angstrom (Å) is 1×10^{-10} meters. Assume that stearic acid is essentially a hydrocarbon chain of 18 carbon atoms. The carbon "backbone" of the molecule is not linear, and zig-zags with bond angles of 109.5°. See the drawings below.

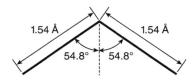

The structure consists of eight and a half "triangles" as drawn below, with a bond angle of 109.5°.

The upper angle of the half triangle is 109.5÷2 = 54.8°, and the sides of the triangle are the bond lengths of 1.54 Angstroms. The sine of 54.8° can be used to calculate the distance between the two carbon atoms at the base of the triangle.

Sine 54.8° = (opposite side) ÷ hypotenuse

= ½ C–C distance of base ÷ (1.54 Angstroms)

Use the above relationship to calculate the length of the stearic acid hydrocarbon chain. Show your work. Remember that the distance between the carbon atoms at the base of the triangle is twice the length of the opposite side in the calculation. There are a total of 8½ "triangles" in the stearic acid molecule.

2. Compare your experimental result for the length of stearic acid to the calculated value in question 1. Make sure the units are the same. Is your experimental value larger or smaller than the calculated value?

3. Provide any sources of error in the experiment.

Appendix

Tables A-1–A-3

Table A-1. Vapor Pressure of Water at Different Temperatures

Temp. (°C)	Vapor Pressure (mm Hg)	Temp. (°C)	Vapor Pressure (mm Hg)
0	4.6	25	23.8
5	6.5	26	25.2
10	9.2	27	26.7
15	12.8	28	28.3
16	13.6	29	30.0
17	14.5	30	31.8
18	15.5	35	42.2
19	16.5	40	55.3
20	17.5	45	71.9
21	18.6	50	92.5
22	19.8	60	149.4
23	2l.1	70	233.7
24	22.4	80	355.1

Table A-2. Temperature Corrections for Barometer Readings

Temp (°C)	Barometer Reading (mm Hg)						
	640	660	680	700	720	740	760
16	1.7	I.7	I.8	1.8	1.9	1.9	2.0
18	1.9	I.9	2.0	2.1	2.1	2.2	2.2
20	2.1	2.2	2.2	2.3	2.3	2.4	2.5
22	2.3	2.4	2.4	2.5	2.6	2.7	2.7
24	2.5	2.6	2.7	2.7	2.8	2.9	3.0
26	2.7	2.8	2.9	3.0	3.0	3.1	3.2
28	2.9	3.0	3.1	3.2	3.3	3.4	3.5
30	3.1	3.2	3.3	3.4	3.5	3.6	3.7

Subtract the corrections from the barometer reading to obtain the atmospheric pressure.

Table A-3. Density of Water at Various Temperatures

Temp. (°C)	Density (g/mL)	Temp. (°C)	Density (g/mL)
0	0.99987	26	0.99681
1	0.99993	27	0.99654
2	0.99997	28	0.99626
3	0.99999	29	0.99597
4	1.00000	30	0.99567
5	0.99999	31	0.99537
6	0.99997	32	0.99505
7	0.99993	33	0.99473
8	0.99988	34	0.99440
9	0.99981	35	0.99406
10	0.99973	36	0.99371
11	0.99963	37	0.99336
12	0.99952	38	0.99299
13	0.99940	39	0.99262
14	0.99927	40	0.99224
15	0.99913	41	0.99186
16	0.99897	42	0.99147
17	0.99880	43	0.99107
18	0.99862	44	0.99066
19	0.99843	45	0.99025
20	0.99823	46	0.98982
21	0.99802	47	0.98940
22	0.99780	48	0.98896
23	0.99756	49	0.98852
24	0.99732	50	0.98807
25	0.99707	51	0.98762

B Appendix

Ionization Constants

Table B-1. Ionization Constants of Weak Acids and Bases

Acids Name	Formula	K_a
acetic acid	CH_3CO_2H	1.8×10^{-5}
ascorbic acid	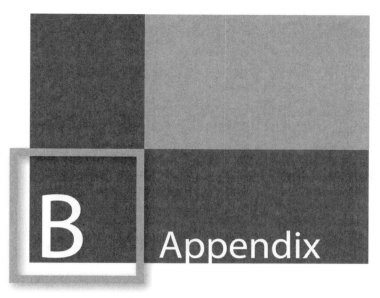	8.0×10^{-5}
benzoic acid		6.5×10^{-5}
carbonic acid	H_2CO_3	4.2×10^{-7}
bicarbonate ion	HCO_3^-	4.8×10^{-11}
oxalic acid	HO_2CCO_2H	6.5×10^{-2}
hydrogen oxalate ion	$HO_2CO_2^-$	6.1×10^{-5}
phosphoric acid	H_3PO_4	7.5×10^{-3}
dihydrogen phosphate ion	$H_2PO_4^-$	6.2×10^{-8}
hydrogen phosphate ion	HPO_4^{2-}	4.8×10^{-13}
propanoic acid	$CH_3CH_2CO_2H$	1.34×10^{-5}
sulfuric acid	H_2SO_4	very strong
hydrogen sulfate ion	HSO_4^-	1.3×10^{-2}
Bases Name	**Formula**	K_b
ammonia	NH_3	1.8×10^{-5}

Appendix B

278

Graphing

In this and other courses, you will sometimes be required to present your data graphically. While the parameters graphed will vary with each experiment, there are some general rules on preparing graphs which should **always** be followed. If these guidelines are ignored, not only will your final results be inaccurate, but you will also lose a significant amount of credit on your laboratory reports. **Computer-generated graphs are not acceptable** unless accompanied by a hand-drawn graph as outlined below.

Guidelines for Graphing

1. Use paper with a 1 mm × 1 mm grid. This paper is available at the university bookstore.

2. The variable being measured goes vertically on the y-axis, and the variable being adjusted by the experimenter goes horizontally on the x-axis. For example, in the density experiment, you will deliver various volumes of a liquid into a beaker. The mass of the liquid portions will then be determined. Since you, as the experimenter, are controlling the volume (the independent variable), volume should be graphed on the x-axis. The mass, which is dependent on the volume delivered, should be graphed on the vertical axis.

3. Axes must be labeled with the units in parenthesis. For the density experiment, the x-axis would be labeled: VOLUME (mL), and the y-axis would be labeled: MASS (g).

4. The graph must have a title written at the very top of the paper. For the density experiment the title might be, "Mass versus Volume Data for Distilled Water."

5. Select a scale for each axis so that the data fills the entire piece of graph paper. If your data should pass through the origin (x=0; y=0), then the lower left corner should be (0,0). However, many graphs do not pass through the origin, so there is no reason to start the graph at (0,0). The scale for the x- and y-axis need not be the same.

6. Data points should be clearly visible. Enclose data points with a circle, box, or triangle so that they are clearly indicated.

7. Never connect the data points to obtain a line. If the data is linear, use a clear plastic ruler (available at the bookstore) so that you can use a straight edge to draw the straight line which best represents your data points. The clear ruler will let you see through to the data points on the graph. If the data suggest a curve, do not draw the curve freehand. Use either a French curve or a flexicurve (a bendable edge) to draw the best smooth curve represented by the data points. Both French curves and flexicurves are available at the bookstore.

8. When determining the slope of a straight line, **never** use data points. Choose two places on the graph where the line crosses grid points on the paper. Use these two points (not data points) to determine the change in y and change in x.

D Appendix

The Operation of Laboratory Burners

A laboratory burner will be used frequently throughout the laboratory course for heating. The correct procedures for lighting and adjusting the burner are outlined below. The burner requires both air (oxygen) and gas in order to work properly. The ratio of gas to air can be adjusted to create very hot flames for intense heating, or flames of lesser intensity for gentle heating.

Below is a sketch of a burner with the various working parts identified.

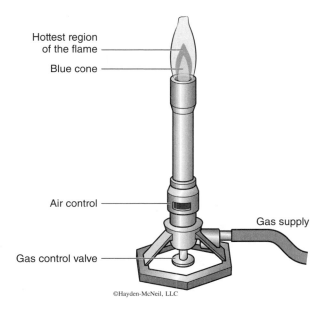

Hottest region of the flame

Blue cone

Air control

Gas supply

Gas control valve

©Hayden-McNeil, LLC

The diagram shows a burner which has been adjusted to produce an intensely hot flame. When properly adjusted, a bright blue cone appears within the flame. The hottest part of the flame is just above the tip of the blue cone. A flame such as this would be used to intensely heat a crucible. It would **not** be used to keep water at a boil or to gently warm the contents of a test tube.

Burner Operation

A. To Light

1. Close the air intake holes by rotating the control until the holes are completely blocked.

2. Turn the gas control knob until it is completely closed by turning the knob so that it screws upward into the burner. Then re-open approximately 2 turns.

3. After connecting the hose to the gas valve, open the gas valve on your laboratory bench. Light the burner with the striker.

4. A luminous yellow flame with an undefined shape should be produced. The flame is yellow because there is insufficient oxygen (remember, the air intake is closed) to fully combust the gas. This type of flame should never be used for heating. At this point, the burner can be adjusted to produce the desired flame.

B. For a Hot Flame

1. Alternately increase the air supply and adjust the gas control knob until the bright blue cone appears in the flame. Adjust so that the cone is about 1.5 to 2 inches high. You will also be able to hear a slight "roaring" sound from the burner when it is at its optimum heat output.

C. For Gradual Heating

1. Follow the directions above for a hot flame.

2. Decrease the air flow then the gas flow (using the knob on the bottom of the burner) until a very small (1/2 inch or less) blue section is produced at the bottom of the flame. This type of flame will keep water boiling gently, without vigorous boiling or splashing.

Illustrated on the following page are a few different types of flames and instructions for adjustment.

D. To Shut Off the Burner

Turn off the gas valve on your laboratory bench.

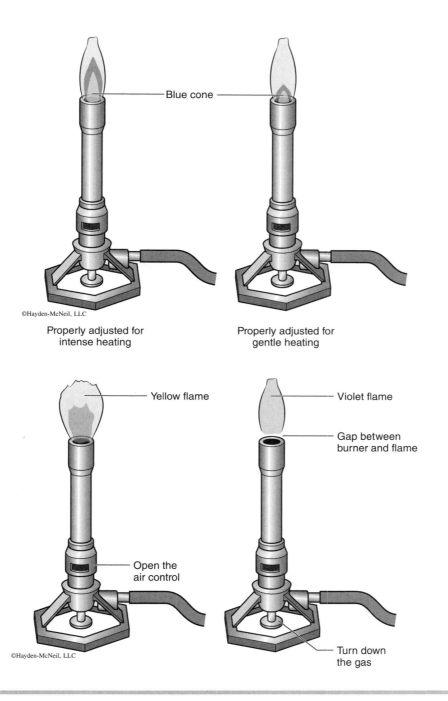

Blue cone

Properly adjusted for
intense heating

Properly adjusted for
gentle heating

©Hayden-McNeil, LLC

Yellow flame

Violet flame

Gap between
burner and flame

Open the
air control

Turn down
the gas

©Hayden-McNeil, LLC

General Rules

Never leave a lit burner unattended. If you are between heatings, turn the burner off and relight it later. Do not leave it burning on the laboratory bench while you are doing other things.

Always make sure you have turned off the gas valve at your laboratory bench before leaving the lab.

Appendix D

284

The Care and Operation of Electronic Analytical Balances

General Care of Balances

The analytical balance is an extremely sensitive scale which can weigh objects to the nearest 0.0001 gram (or tenth of a milligram) accurately. It is a very delicate instrument, and must be used with proper care. Observe the following practices to ensure that balances remain in good working order and accurate weights are obtained.

1. You will be assigned to use a specific balance for the entire semester. All weighings should be done on the same balance. Report any malfunctions to your instructor.

2. Each balance has been positioned, leveled, and adjusted. Do not move a balance even slightly. Pressure applied to the balance table by hands, elbows, or leaning against the table will produce false weights.

3. Press all switches gently and slowly as outlined below.

4. All weighings are by the "difference method." That is, a container plus contents are weighed, some or all of the contents removed, and the container reweighed. The difference in mass equals the mass of contents removed.

5. Chemicals are **never** added to or removed from weighing containers while inside the balance.

6. Balance doors must be closed when weighing and adjusting the controls of the balance. Drafts and air circulation will give an incorrect mass. Likewise, objects must be at room temperature to be weighed accurately. Warm objects create drafts within the chamber and produce false results.

7. The balance must be adjusted to zero before **each** weight is obtained. Do not assume a balance is properly zeroed. See the weighing procedure which follows for the procedure used to zero a balance.

8. When finished weighing clean up any spills in the area of the balance, discard any Kimwipes, and close the compartment doors.

Weighing Procedure

Before using the balance, read the guidelines on general operating procedures and the general care of the balances.

Operation of the Electronic Analytical Balances

1. The balance should be left on during the laboratory period. If it was accidentally switched off, turn on the balance by gently pushing down on the right side of the bar switch. Wait for the display to register all eights, four dash lines (----), and then 0.0000 g before proceeding.

2. With the doors of the balance closed, gently press down on the left side of the bar switch where it says "re-zero." Wait until the digital display reads "0.0000 g."

3. Open the balance door, place the object to be weighed on the pan, close the doors, and wait for a steady reading on the digital display. **NOTE:** Samples are always weighed in a container. Never place chemicals directly on the balance pan.

4. After recording the mass, remove the object from the pan and close the balance doors. Use the same balance for all subsequent weighings.

5. For repeat weighings, zero the balance before **each** weighing.

Spectronic 20 Operating Instructions

1. Turn on the power using the "zero control" knob. Allow 5 minutes for the instrument to warm up and stabilize. Clean both the solvent cell and solution cell and fill them to the mark (about halfway) with the appropriate liquid. Dry the outside of both cells with Kimwipes and handle them only on the upper edge.

2. Set the instrument to the specified wavelength using the wavelength control knob.

3. Adjust the "zero control" knob until the needle reads 0% transmittance.

4. Insert the solvent cell in the cell compartment making sure you align the vertical line on the cell with the line on the cell holder. Close the cover.

5. Adjust the needle to give a reading of 100% transmittance by adjusting the "100% control knob."

6. Remove the solvent cell and insert the solution cell into the holder, close the cover, and read the % transmittance.

7. Return the solvent cell to the cell holder, close the cover, and check that the instrument still reads 100% transmittance with pure solvent.

8. When measuring several solutions, repeat steps 4–7, provided the wavelength and 100% transmittance knobs have not been changed.

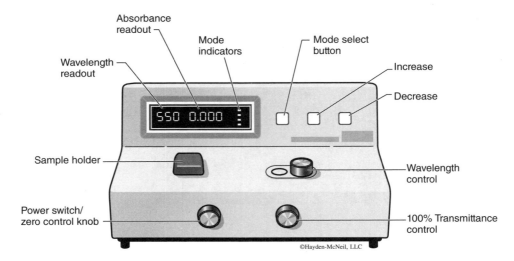

Figure F-1. Spectronic 20 spectrophotometer.

Appendix G

Laboratory Locker Equipment

290

Name   Semester

Course   Section #   Locker #

Chemistry Laboratory Locker Equipment

# of Items	Description	In	Out	# of Items	Description	In	Out
1	Glass Beaker, 100 mL			1	Tripod		
2	Glass Beaker, 150 mL			1	Weighing Bottle		
2	Glass Beaker, 250 mL			1	Wash Bottle, plastic		
2	Glass Beaker, 400 mL			1	Laboratory Burner		
2	Glass Beaker, 600 mL			1	Bottle, 500 mL		
2	Plastic Beaker, 100 mL			1	Ring, medium		
2	Plastic Beaker, 250 mL			1	Ring Stand		
2	Plastic Beaker, 400 mL			1	Clamp		
2	Flasks, Erlenmeyer, 250 mL			1	Clamp Holder		
1	Tubing, 2 feet			1	Test Tube Holder		
10	Test Tubes, 75 × 10 mm			2	Thumb Cots		
10	Test Tubes, 100 × 13 mm			1	Striker with Flint		
9	Test Tubes, 125 × 15 mm			1	Tongs		
2	Test Tubes, 150 × 25 mm			1	Small Brush		
1	Test Tube Rack			1	Large Brush		
1	Graduated Cylinder, 10 mL			1	Wire Gauze		
1	Graduated Cylinder, 50 mL			2	Watch Glasses, 2"		
1	Funnel			2	Watch Glasses, 4"		
1	Rubber Policeman			2	Stirring Rods		
1	24-well Plate			5	Microdroppers		
1	96-well Plate						

To check out of laboratory:

Make sure all of the above items are present, clean, and unbroken. Obtain replacement items from the "extras" in the boxes in the laboratory. If the item you need isn't in one of the boxes, get a replacement from the stockroom.

Appendix G

292

Name   Semester

Course   Section #   Locker #

Chemistry Laboratory Locker Equipment

# of Items	Description	In	Out	# of Items	Description	In	Out
1	Glass Beaker, 100 mL			1	Tripod		
2	Glass Beaker, 150 mL			1	Weighing Bottle		
2	Glass Beaker, 250 mL			1	Wash Bottle, plastic		
2	Glass Beaker, 400 mL			1	Laboratory Burner		
2	Glass Beaker, 600 mL			1	Bottle, 500 mL		
2	Plastic Beaker, 100 mL			1	Ring, medium		
2	Plastic Beaker, 250 mL			1	Ring Stand		
2	Plastic Beaker, 400 mL			1	Clamp		
2	Flasks, Erlenmeyer, 250 mL			1	Clamp Holder		
1	Tubing, 2 feet			1	Test Tube Holder		
10	Test Tubes, 75 × 10 mm			2	Thumb Cots		
10	Test Tubes, 100 × 13 mm			1	Striker with Flint		
9	Test Tubes, 125 × 15 mm			1	Tongs		
2	Test Tubes, 150 × 25 mm			1	Small Brush		
1	Test Tube Rack			1	Large Brush		
1	Graduated Cylinder, 10 mL			1	Wire Gauze		
1	Graduated Cylinder, 50 mL			2	Watch Glasses, 2"		
1	Funnel			2	Watch Glasses, 4"		
1	Rubber Policeman			2	Stirring Rods		
1	24-well Plate			5	Microdroppers		
1	96-well Plate						

To check out of laboratory:

Make sure all of the above items are present, clean, and unbroken. Obtain replacement items from the "extras" in the boxes in the laboratory. If the item you need isn't in one of the boxes, get a replacement from the stockroom.

Appendix G

294

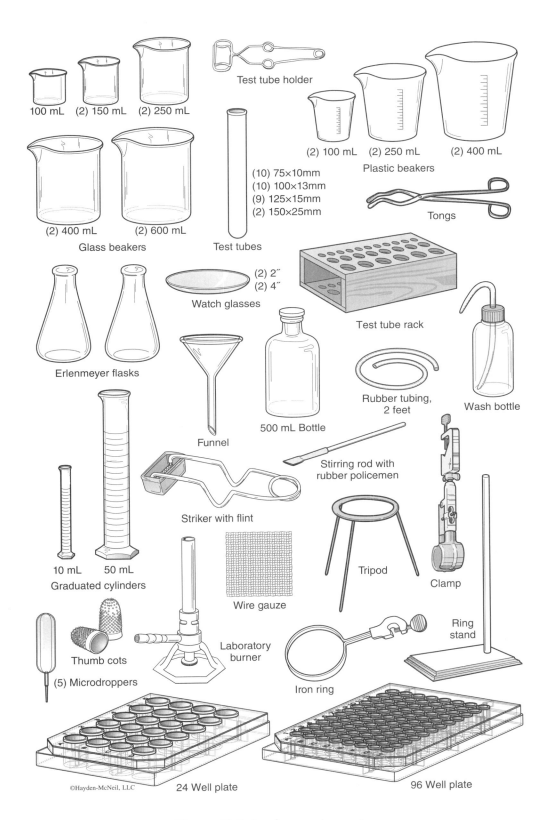

Figure G-1. Locker equipment.

Appendix G

296

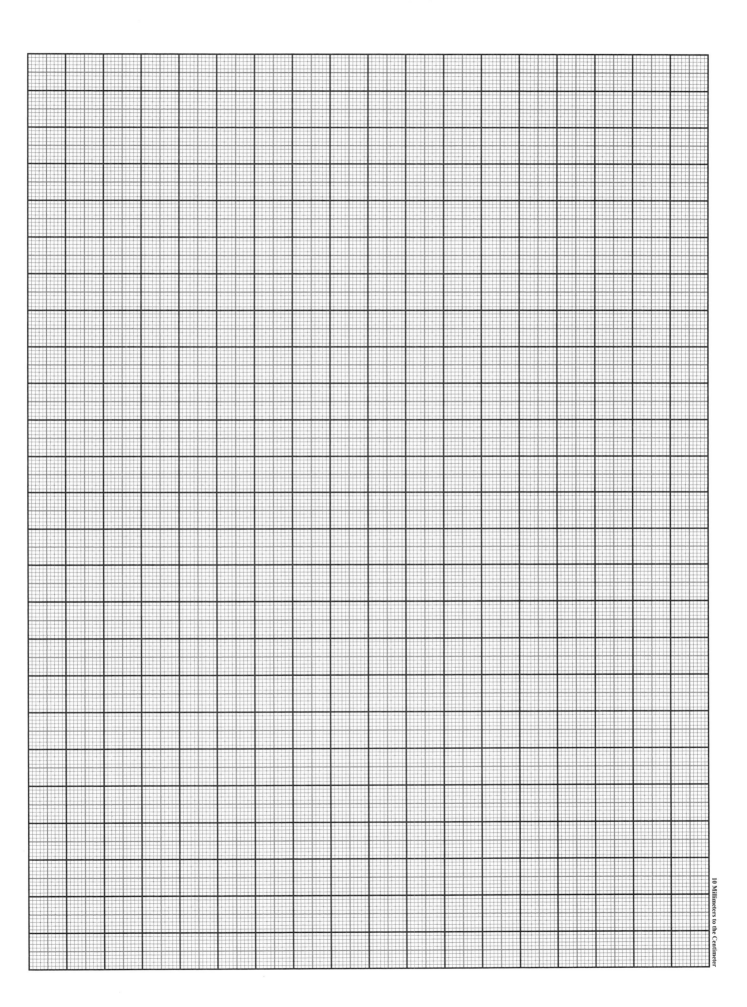

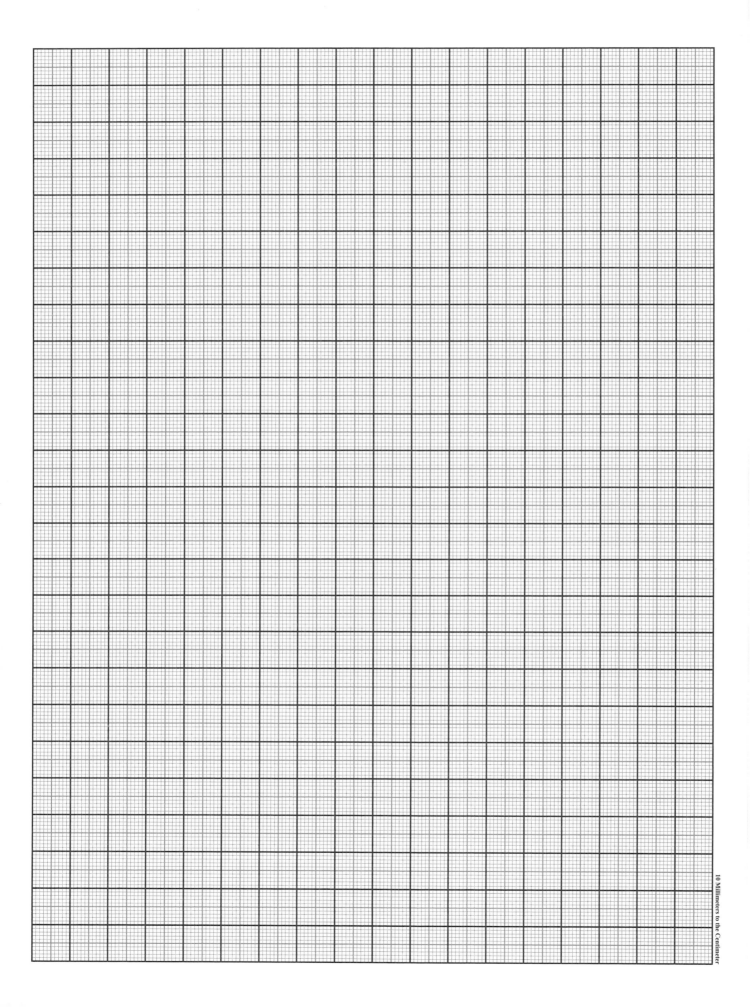

10 Millimeters to the Centimeter

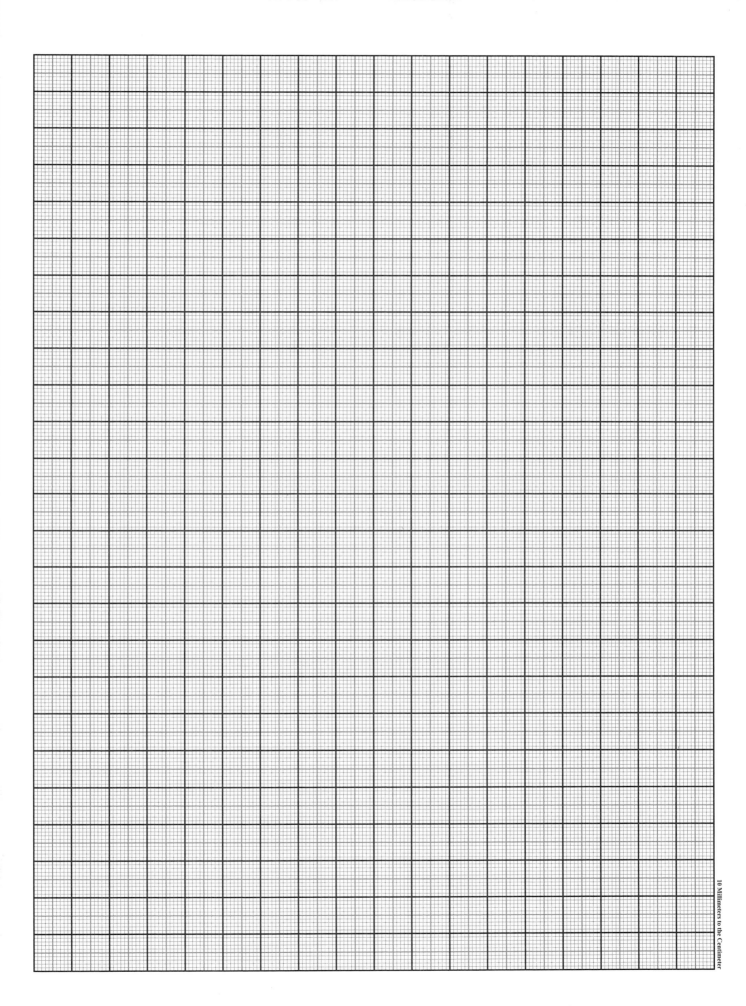

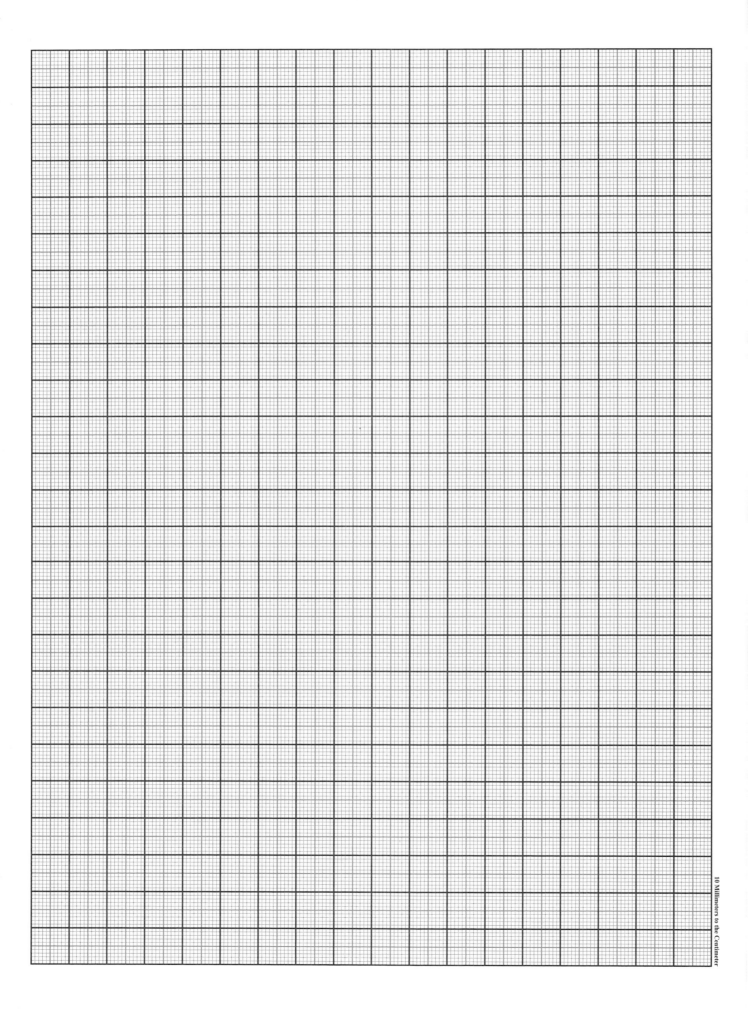

10 Millimeters to the Centimeter

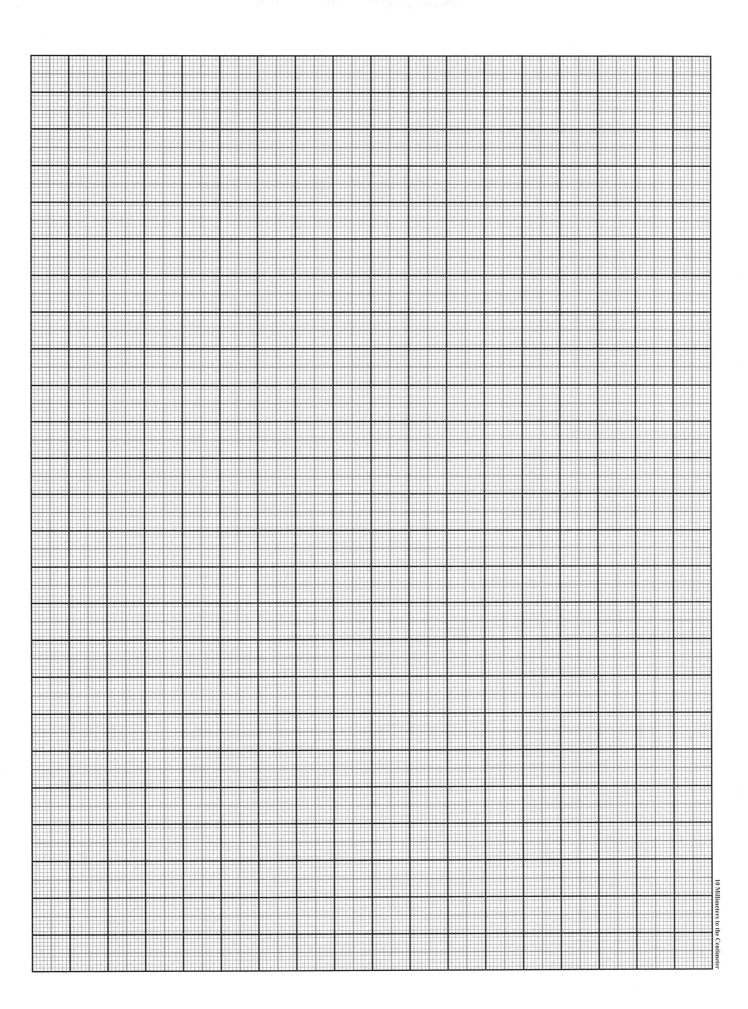

10 Millimeters to the Centimeter

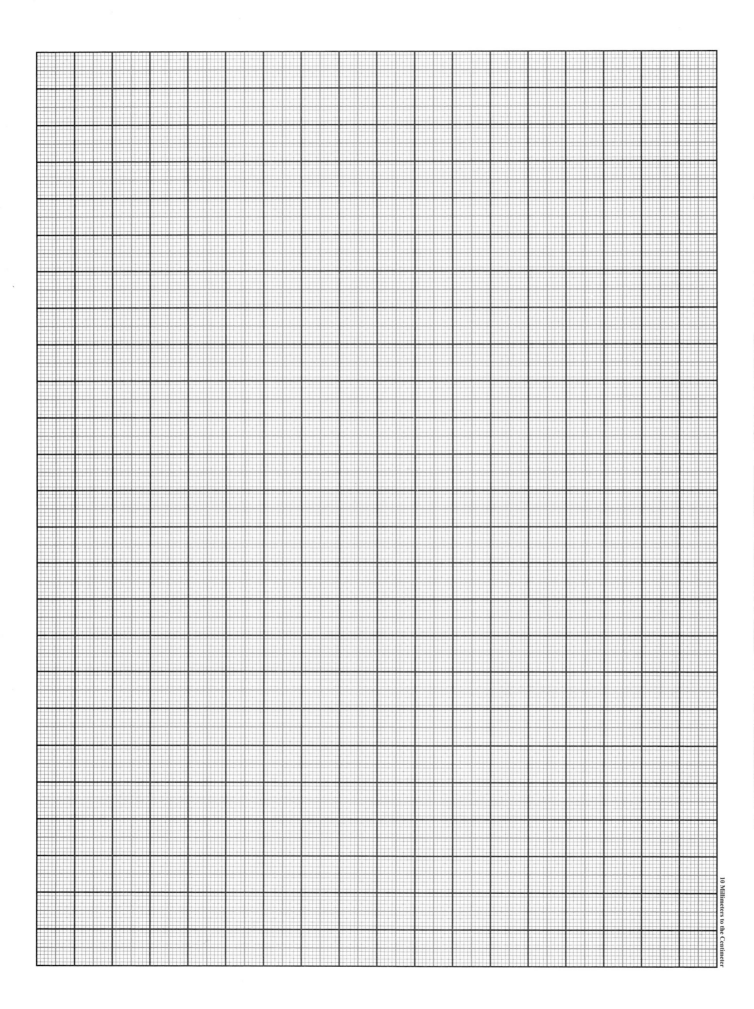

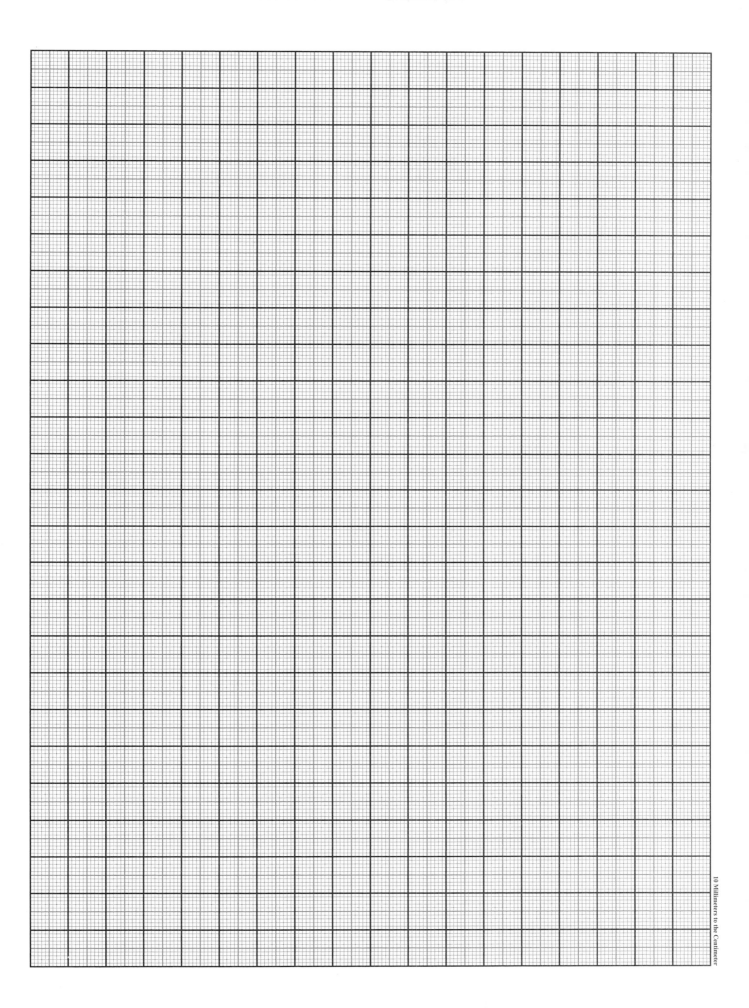

10 Millimeters to the Centimeter

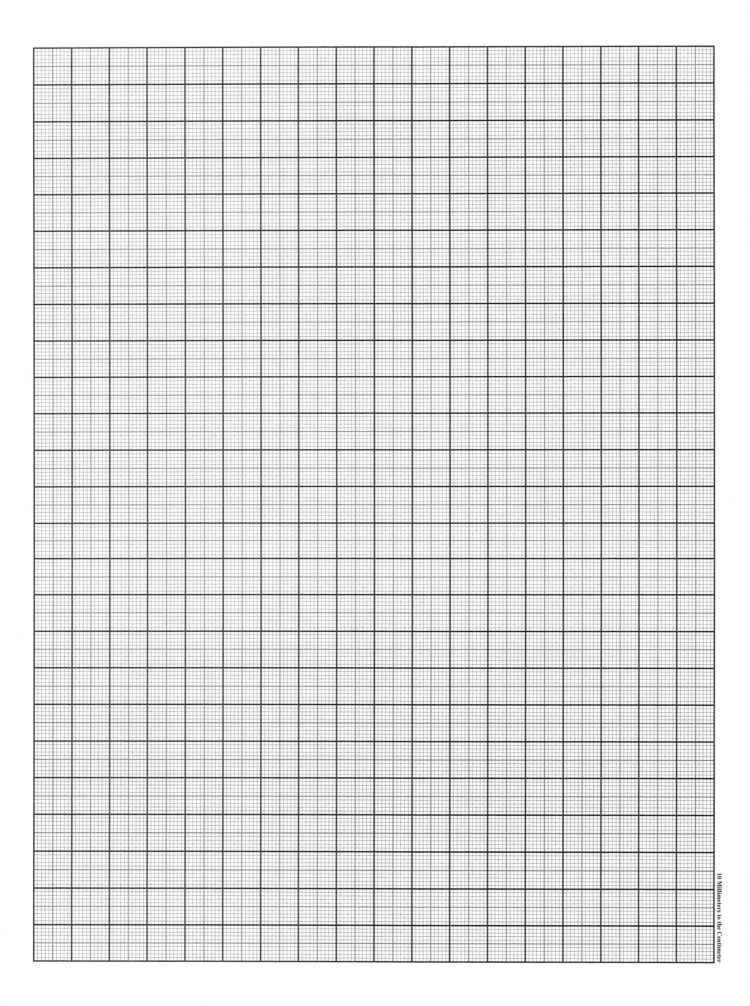

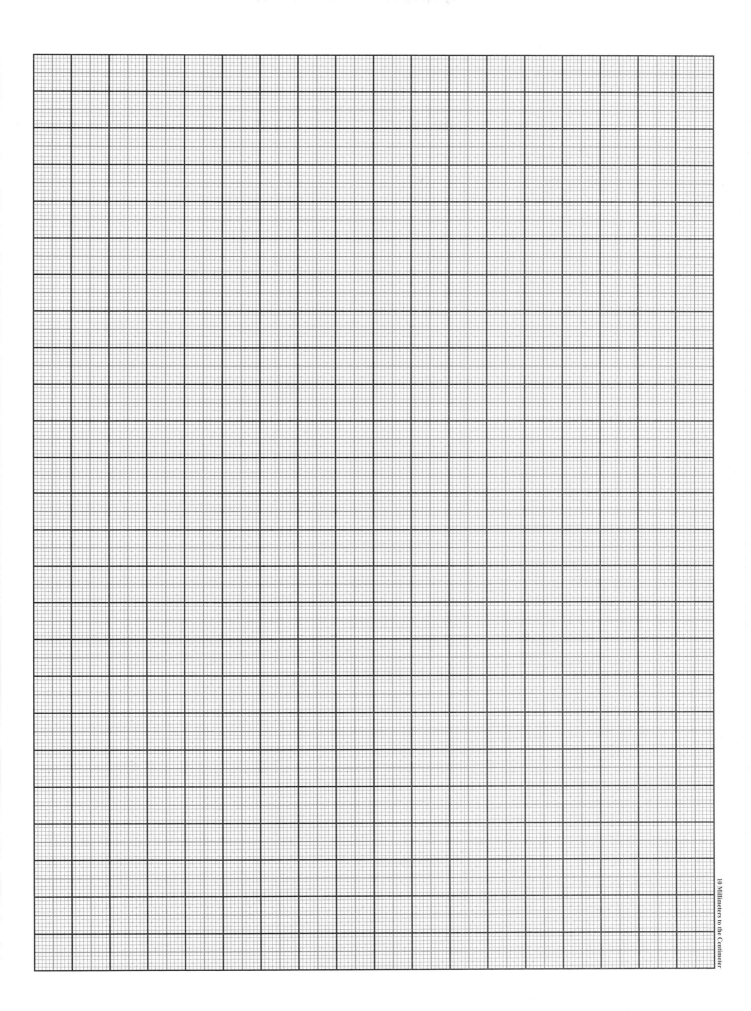

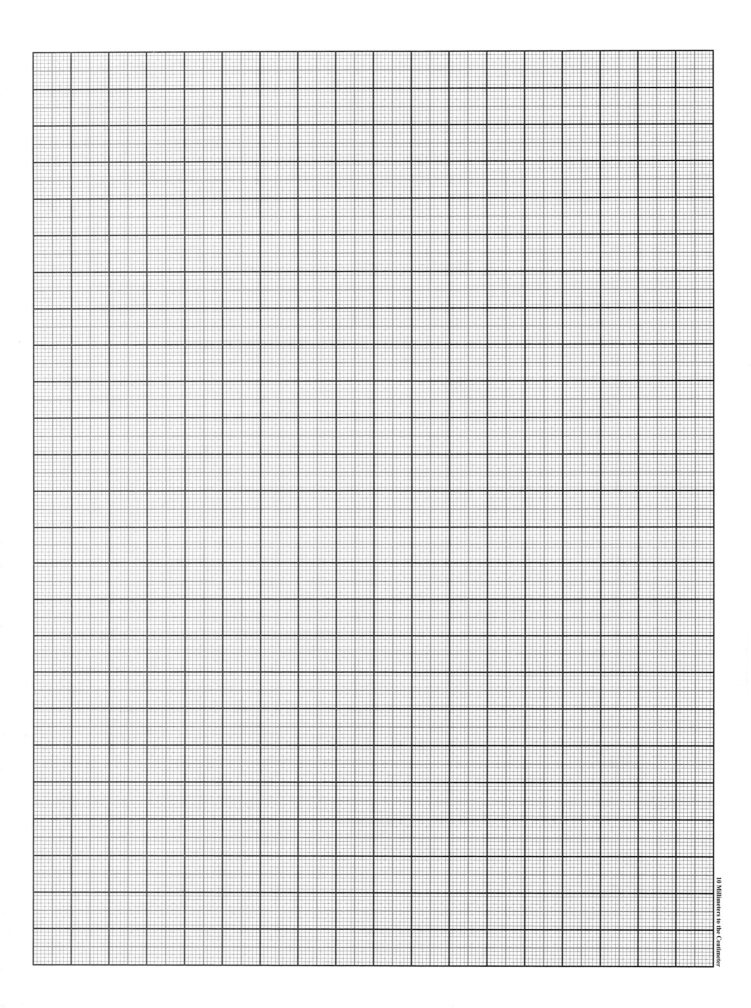

10 Millimeters to the Centimeter

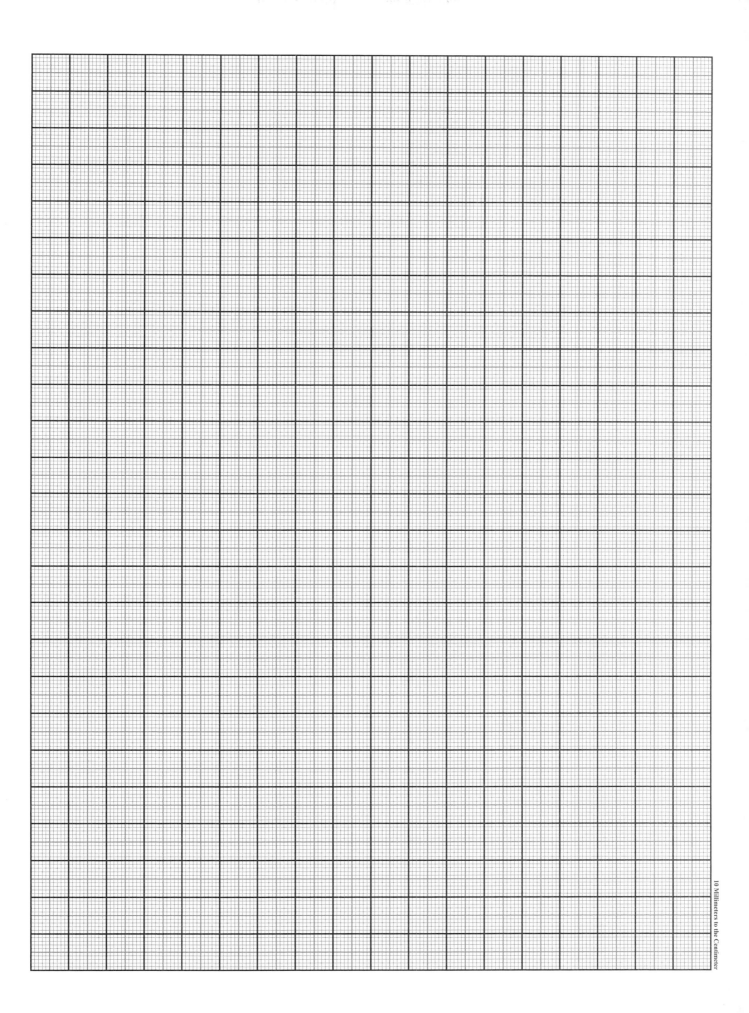

10 Millimeters to the Centimeter

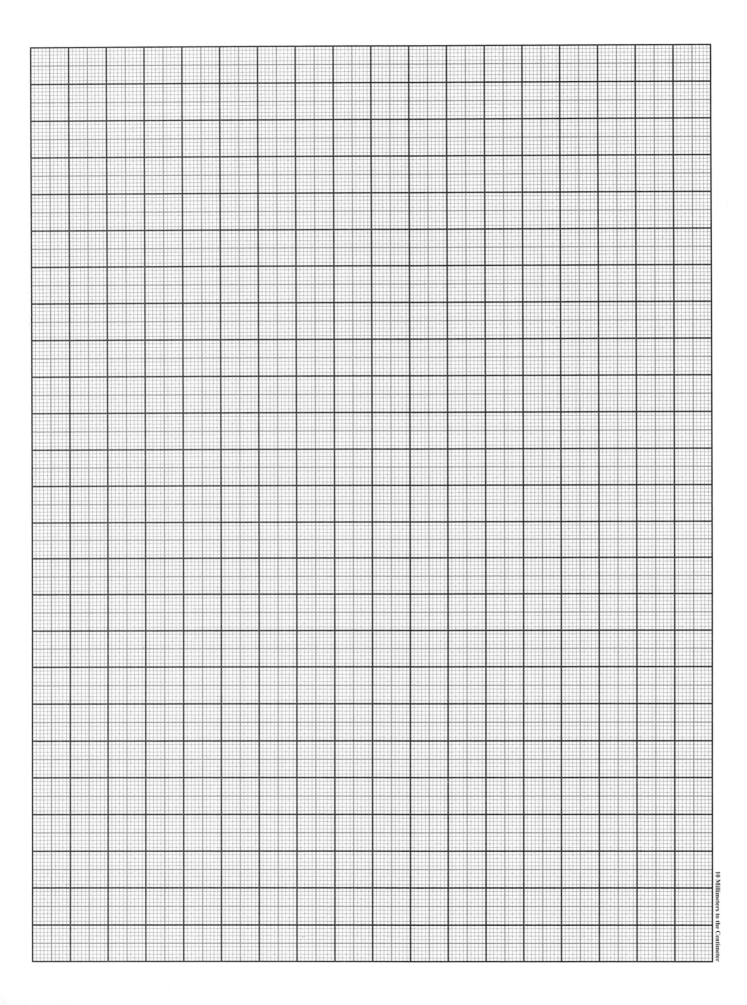

10 Millimeters to the Centimeter

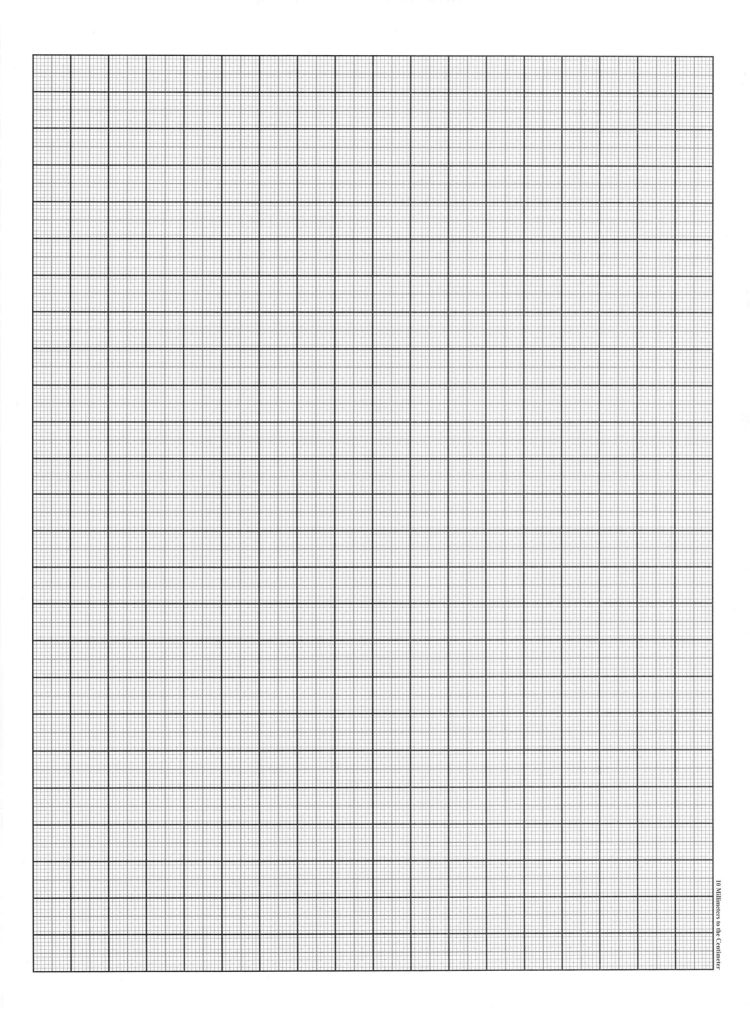

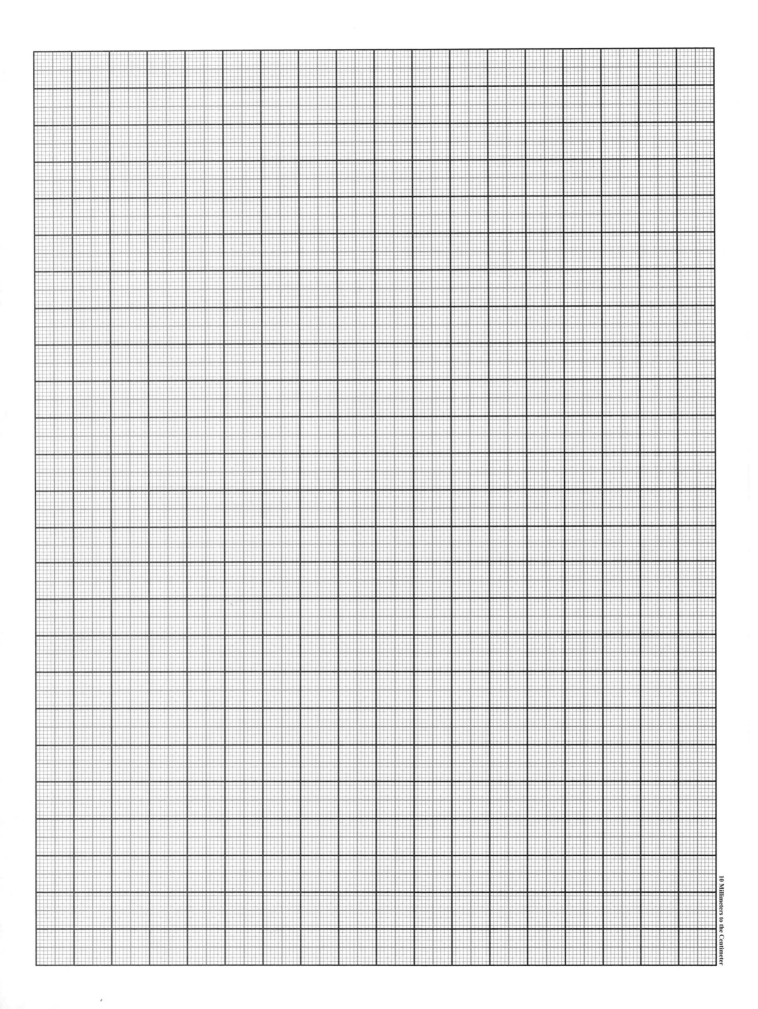

10 Millimeters to the Centimeter

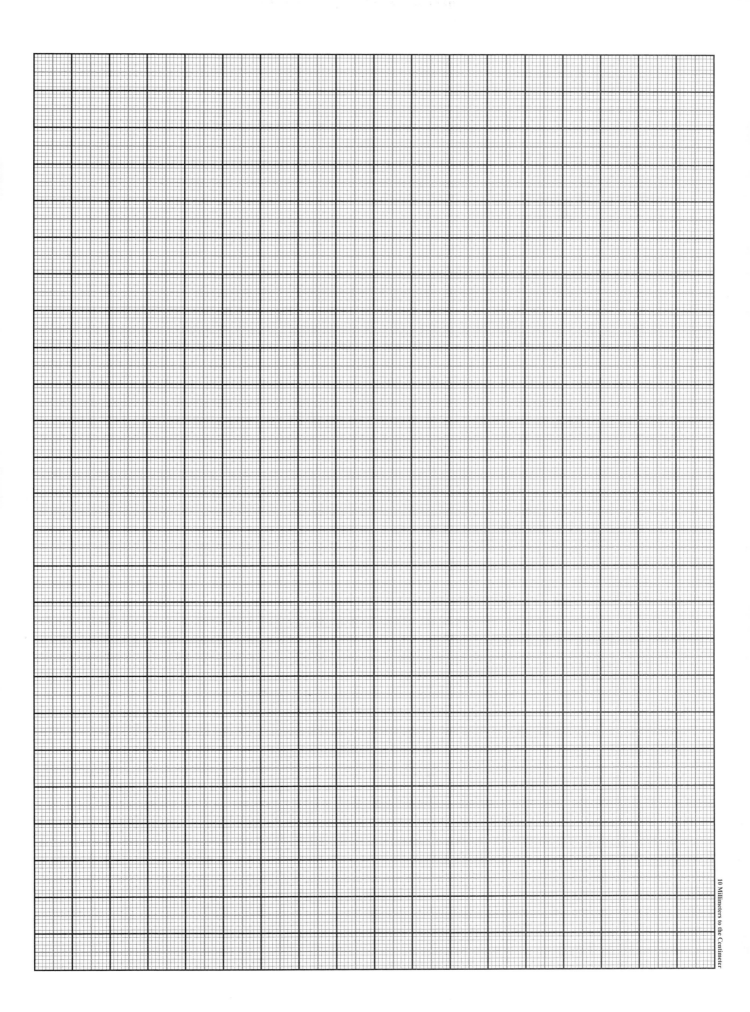

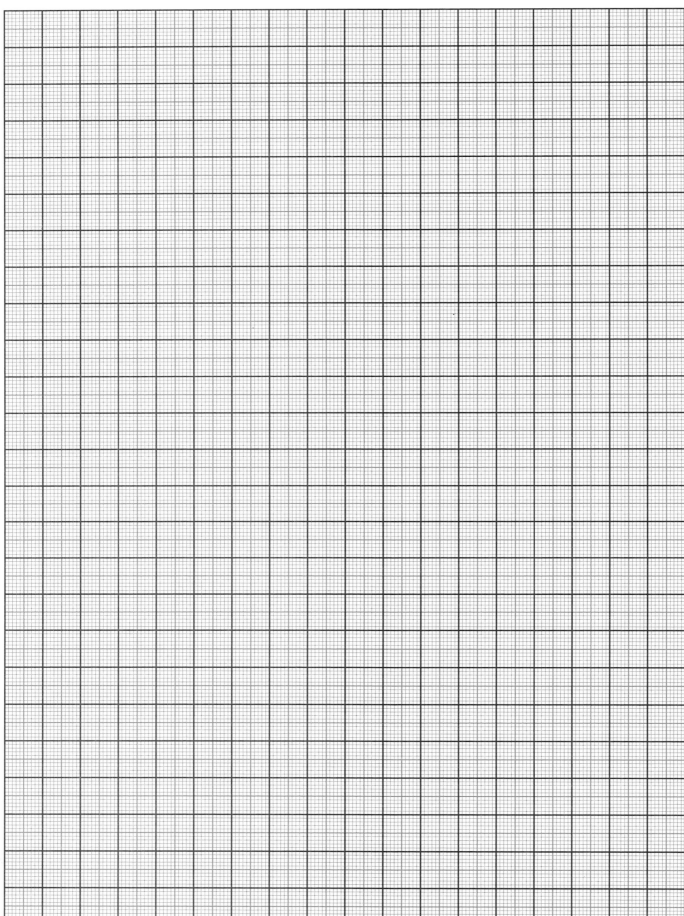

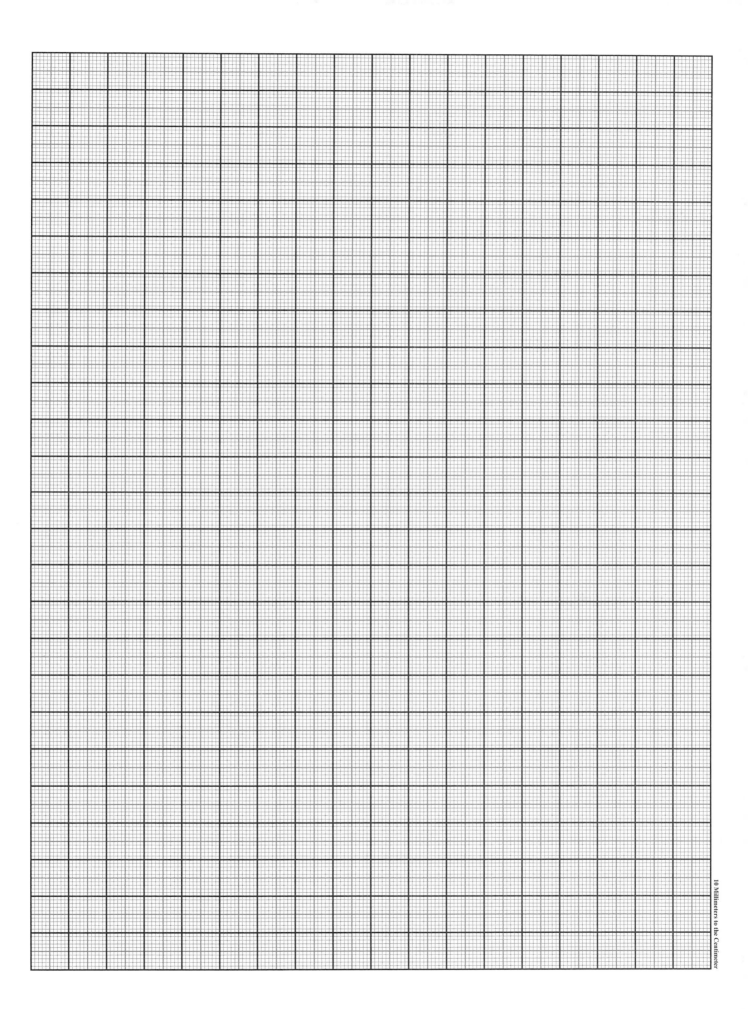

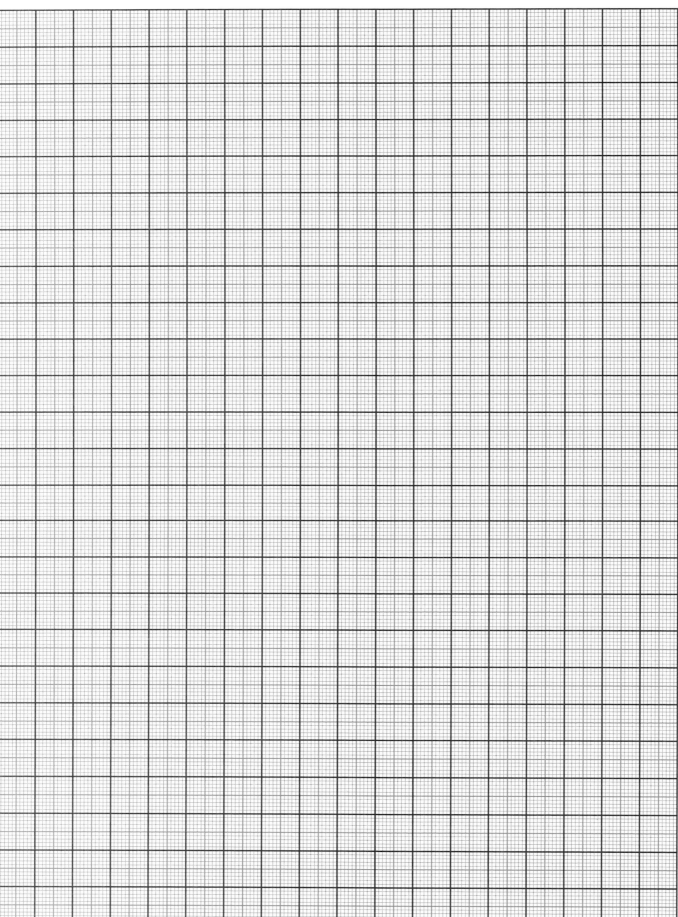

10 Millimeters to the Centimeter

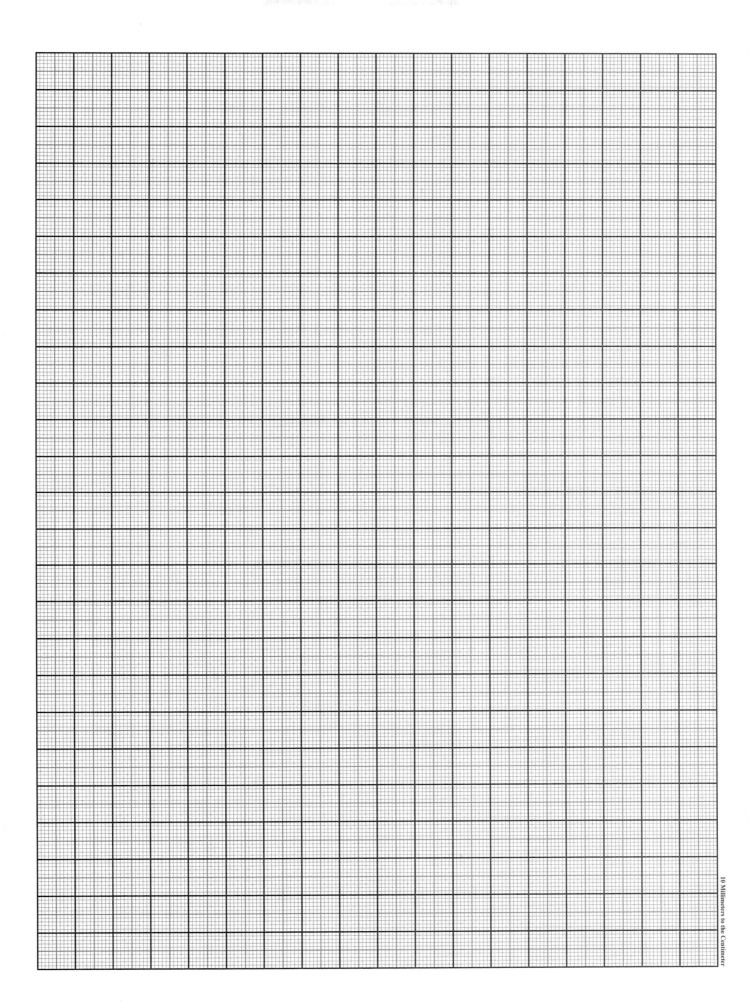

10 Millimeters to the Centimeter

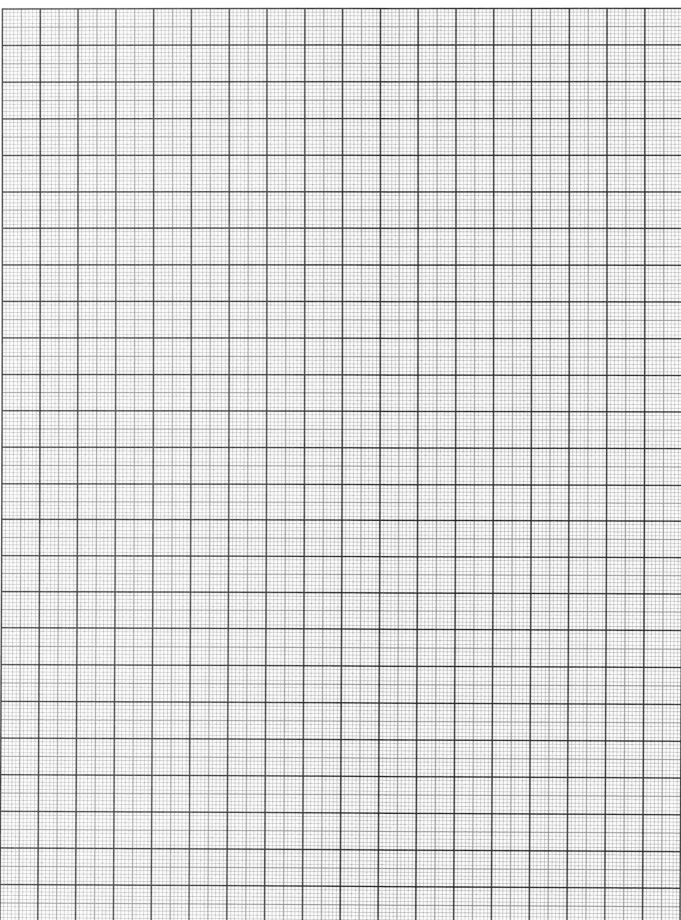

10 Millimeters to the Centimeter

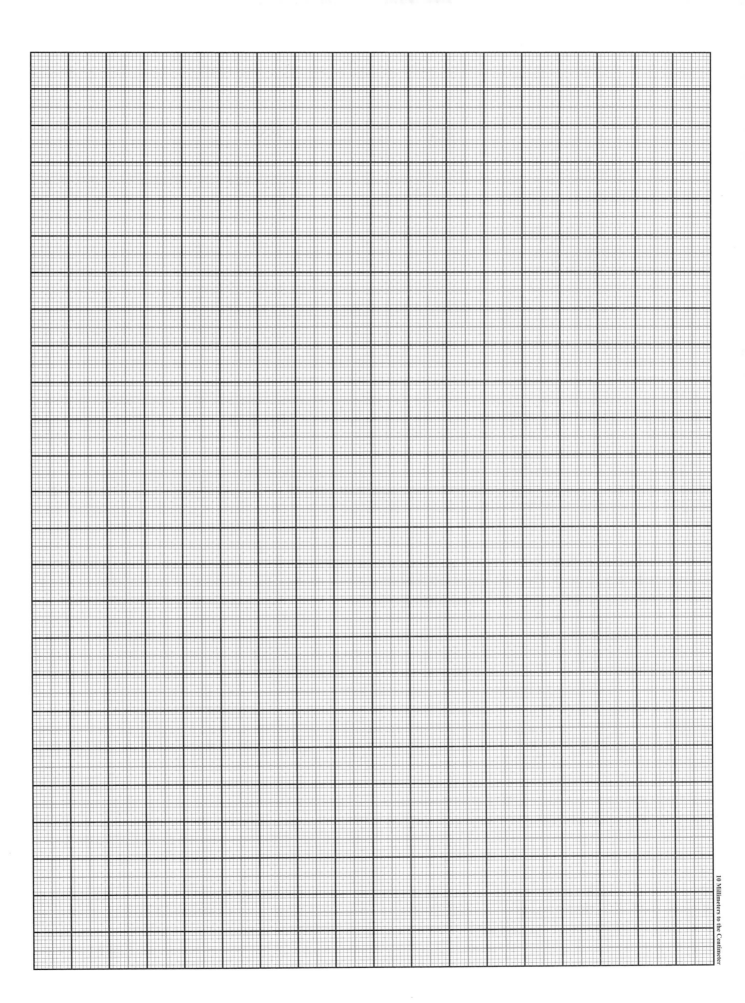

10 Millimeters to the Centimeter

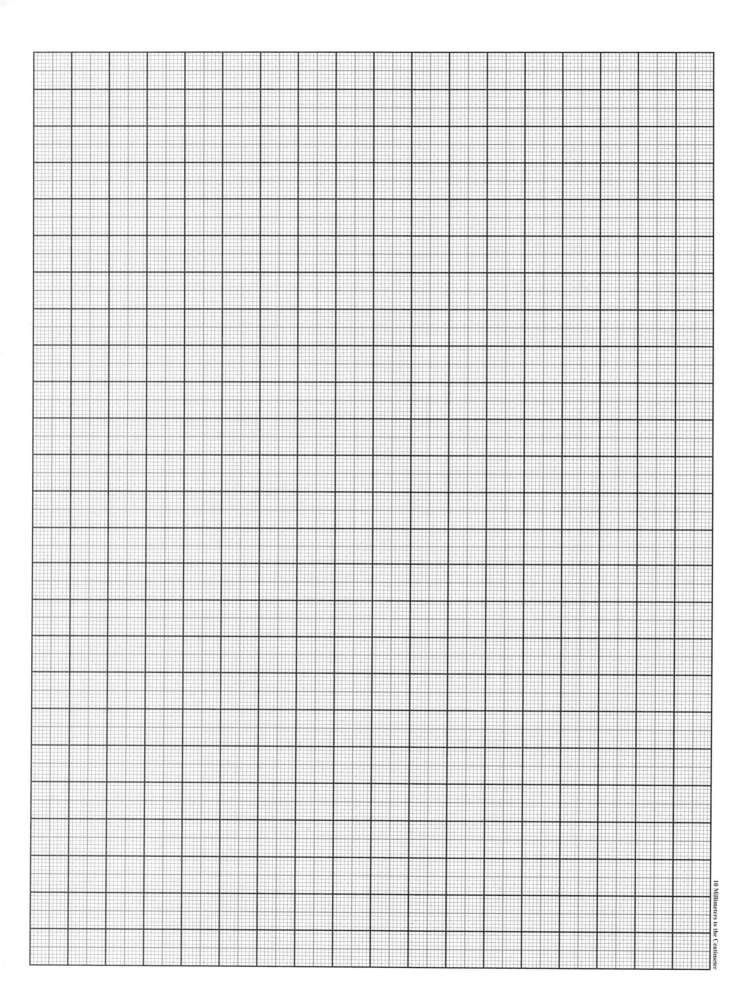

10 Millimeters to the Centimeter

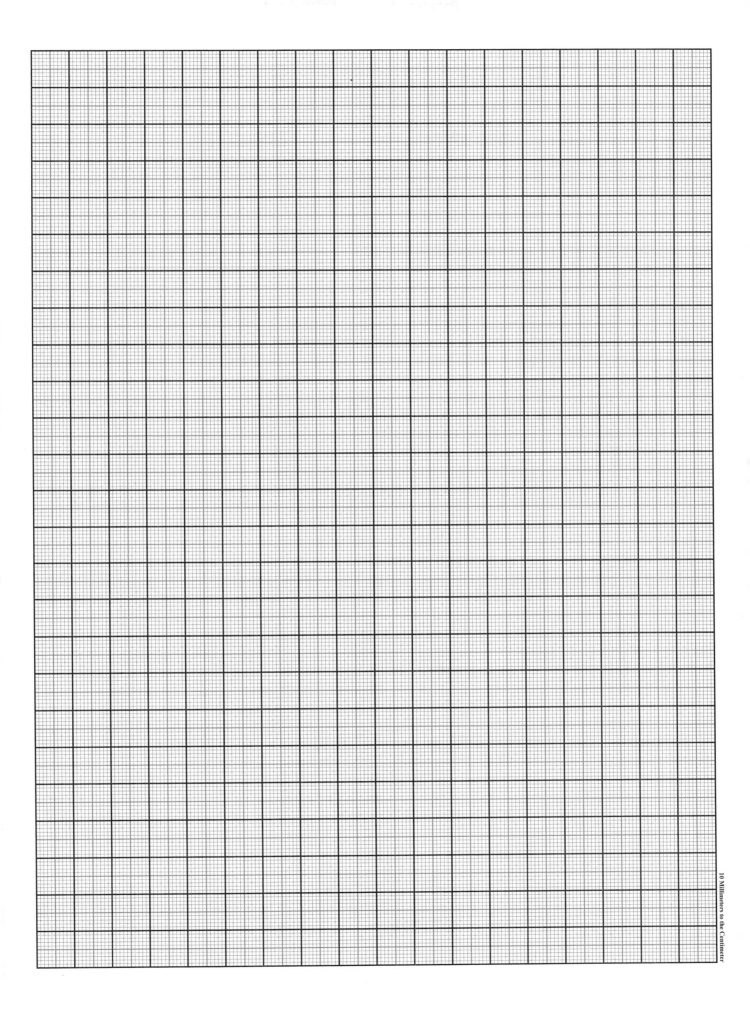

10 Millimeters to the Centimeter

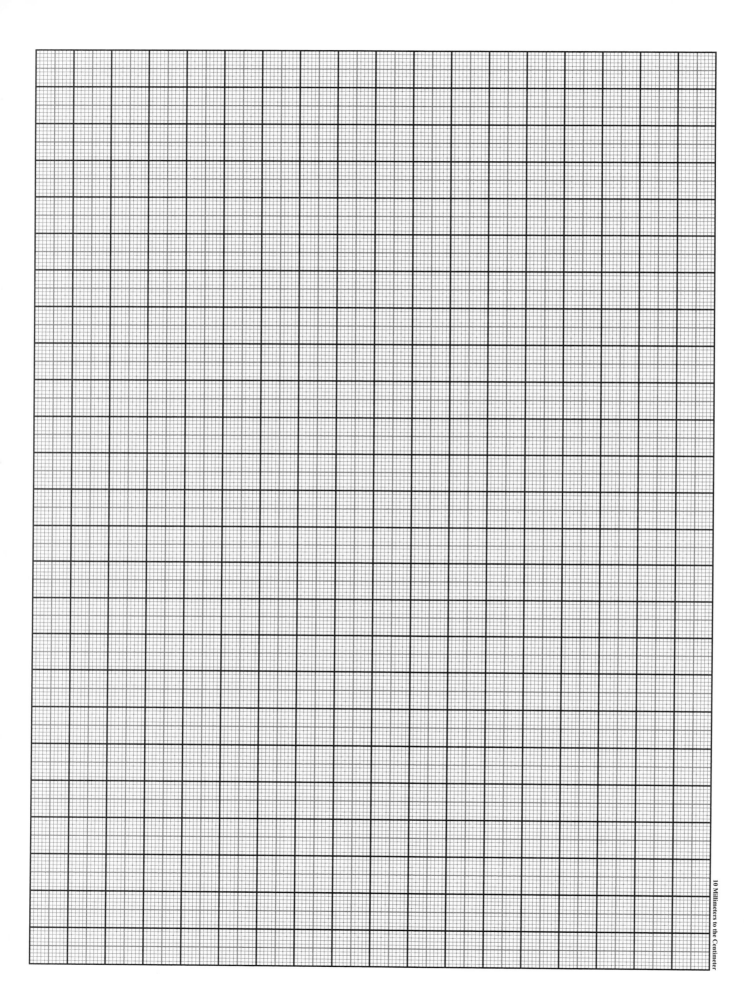

10 Millimeters to the Centimeter

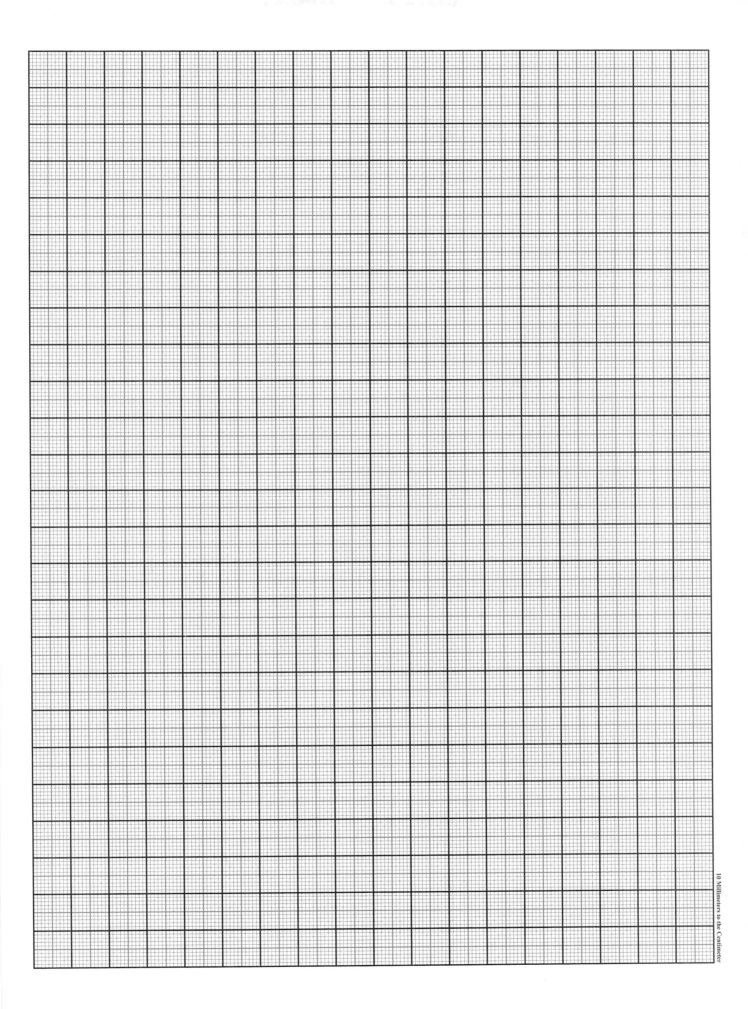

10 Millimeters to the Centimeter

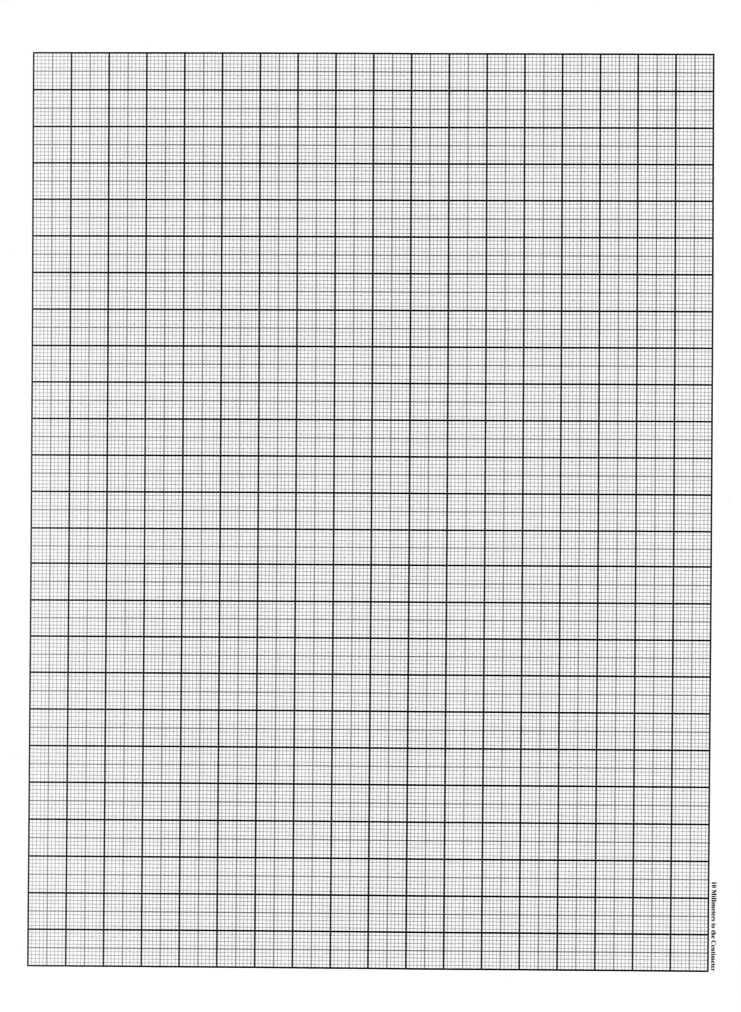

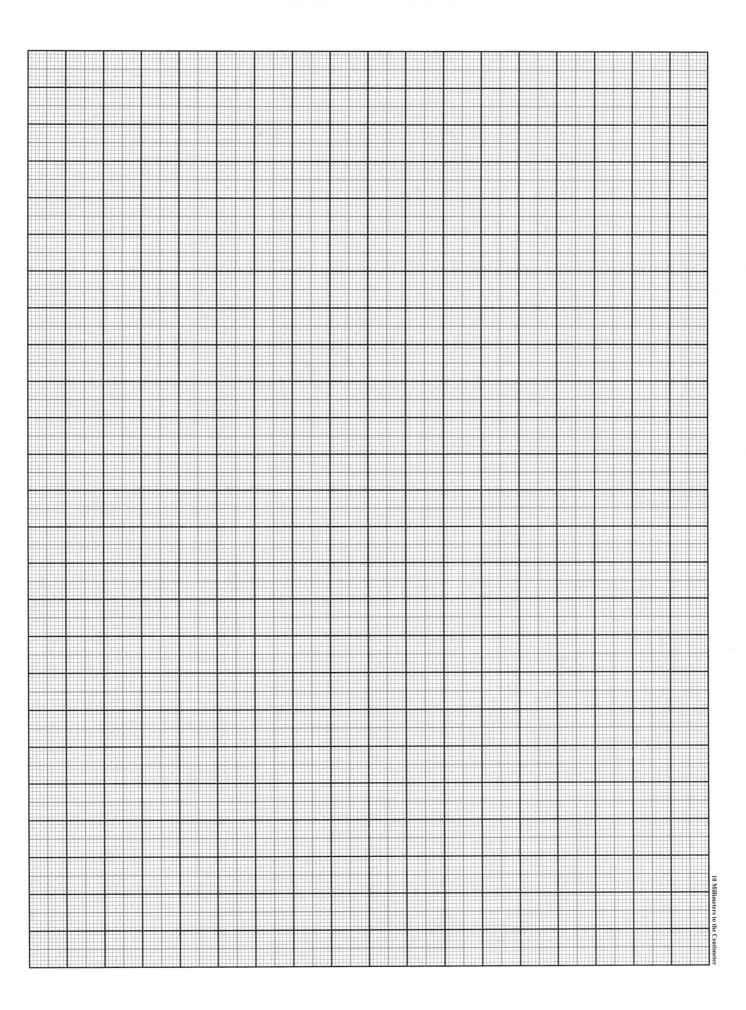

10 Millimeters to the Centimeter

10 Millimeters to the Centimeter

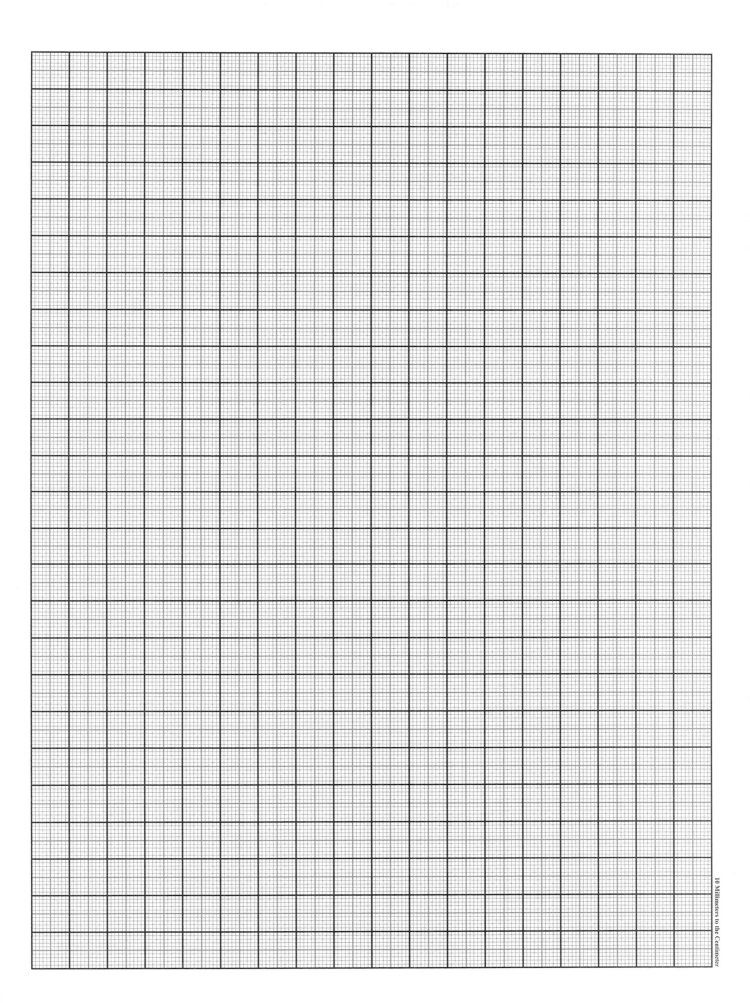

10 Millimeters to the Centimeter

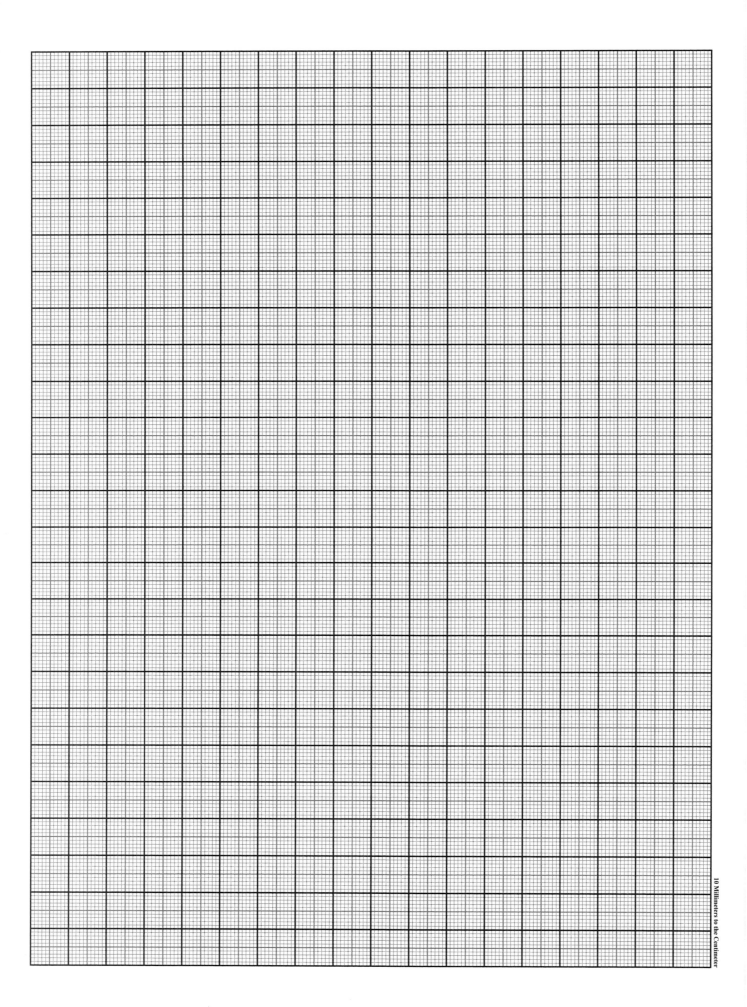

10 Millimeters to the Centimeter

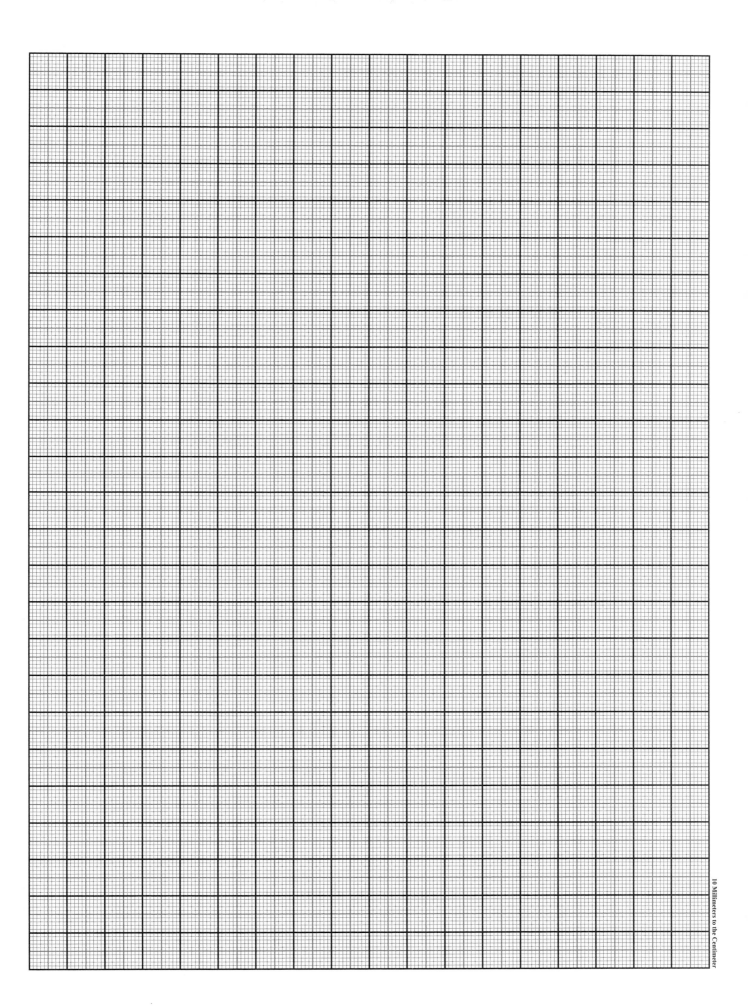

10 Millimeters to the Centimeter

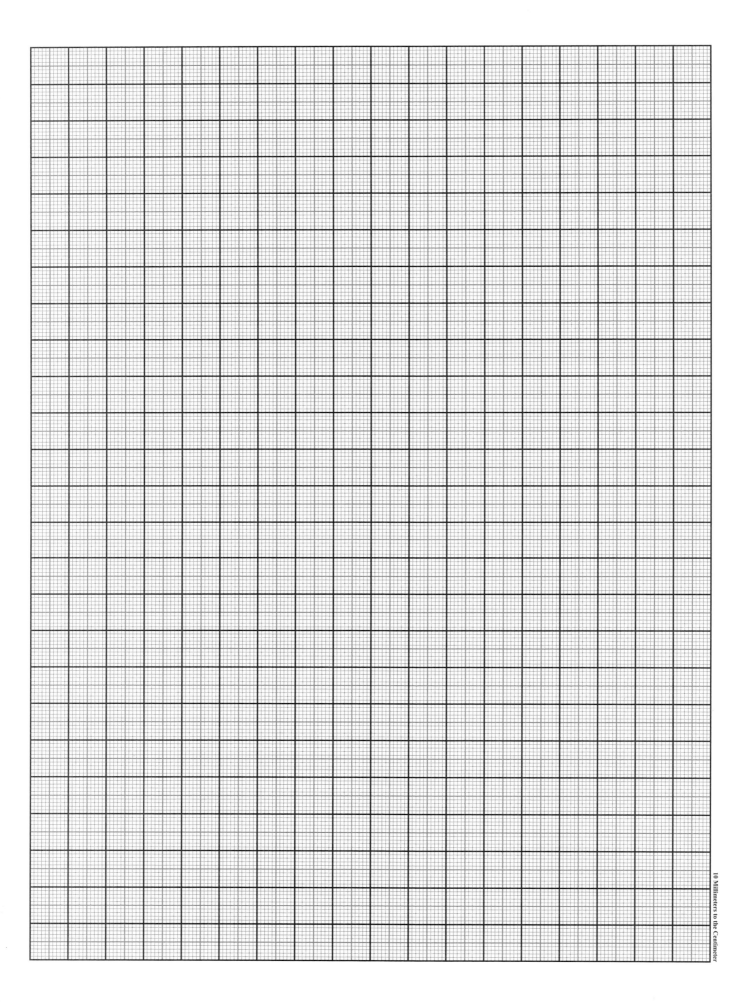

10 Millimeters to the Centimeter

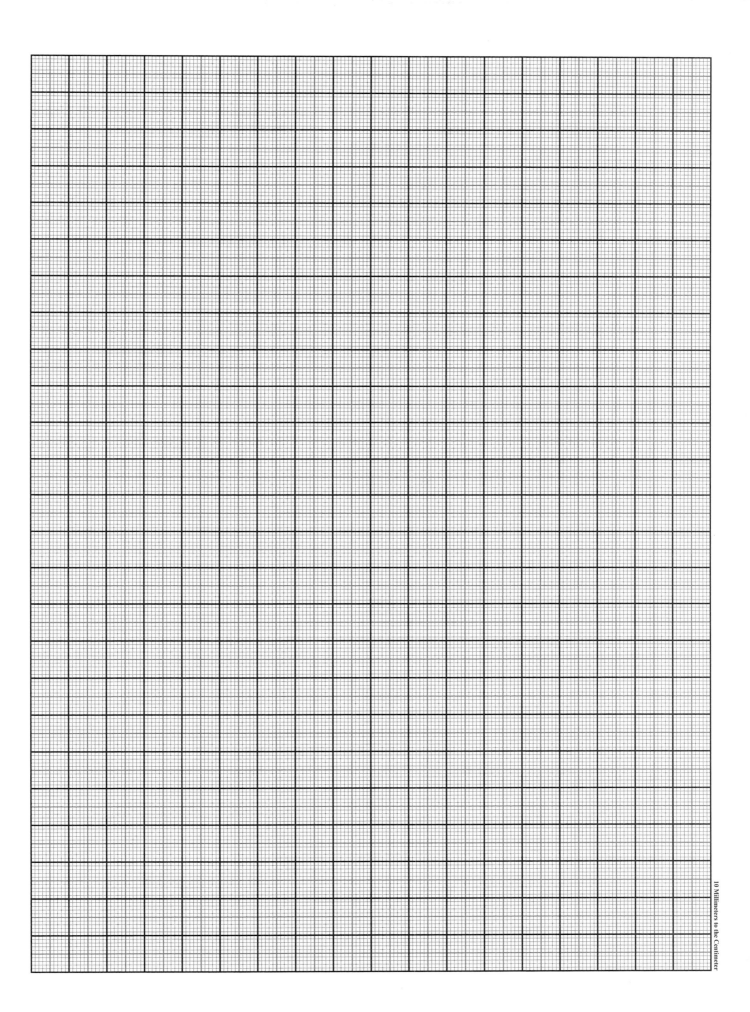

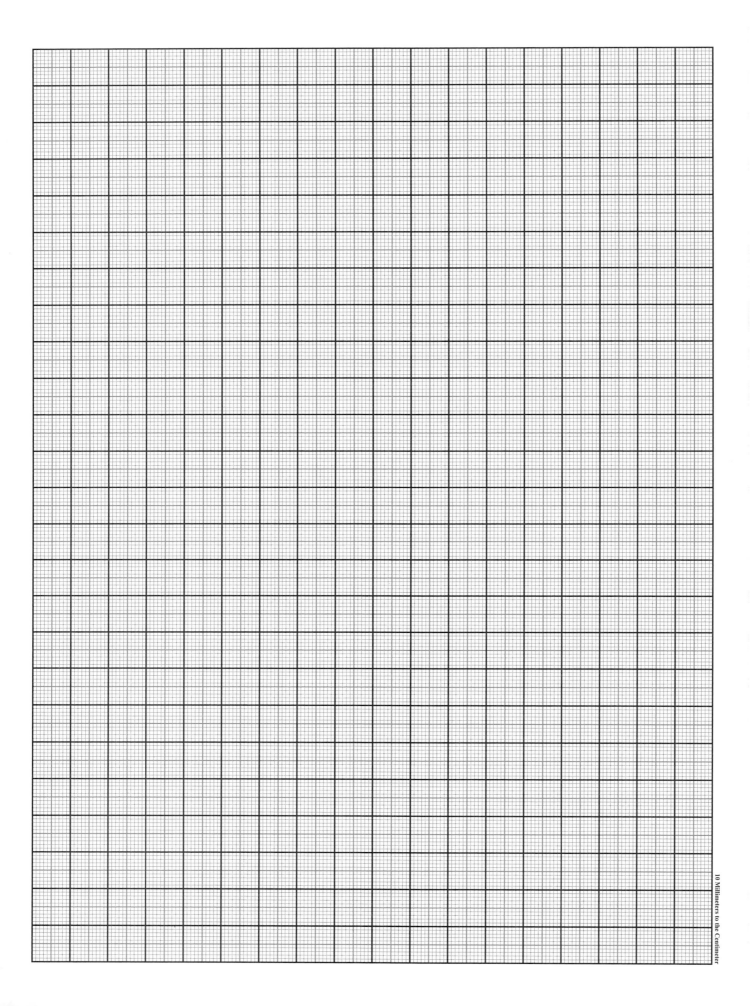

10 Millimeters to the Centimeter

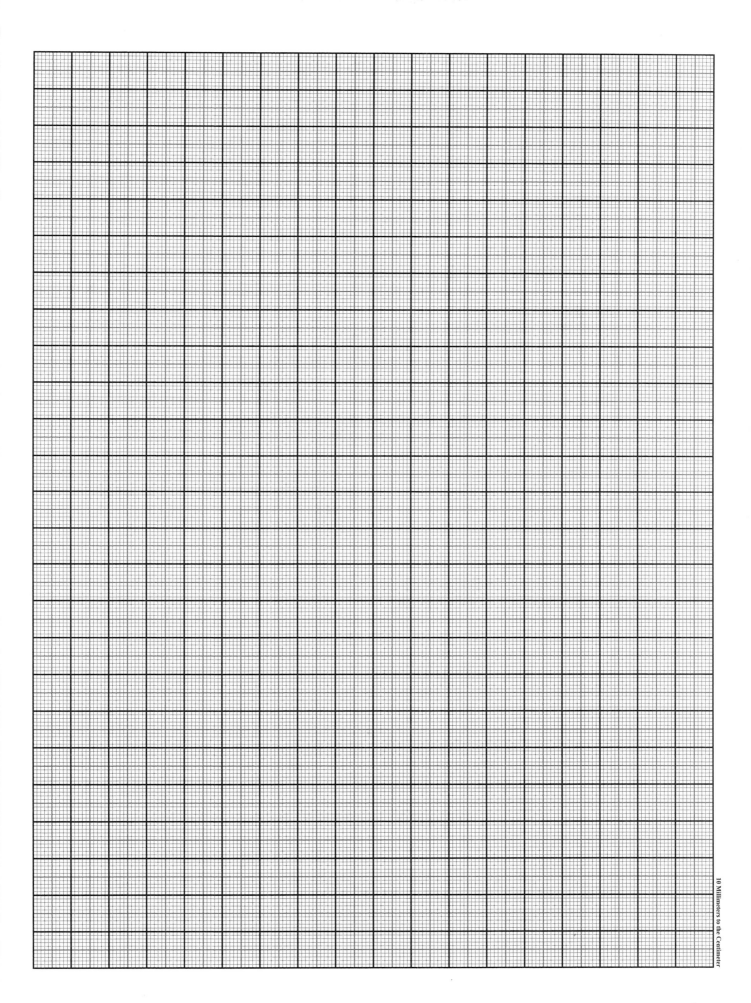

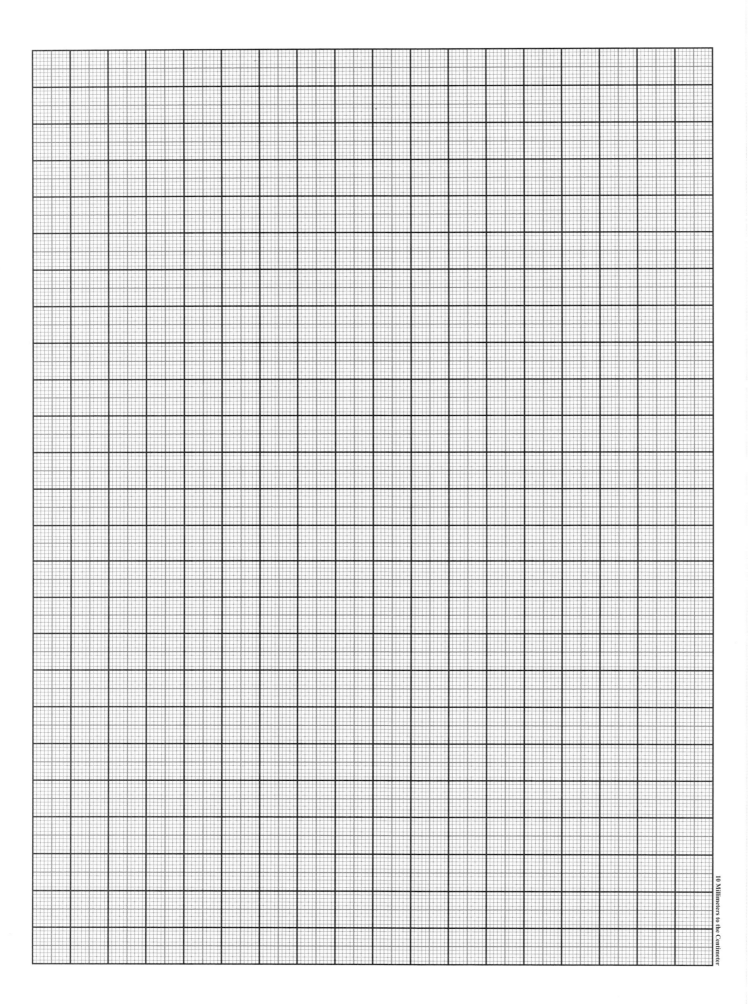

10 Millimeters to the Centimeter

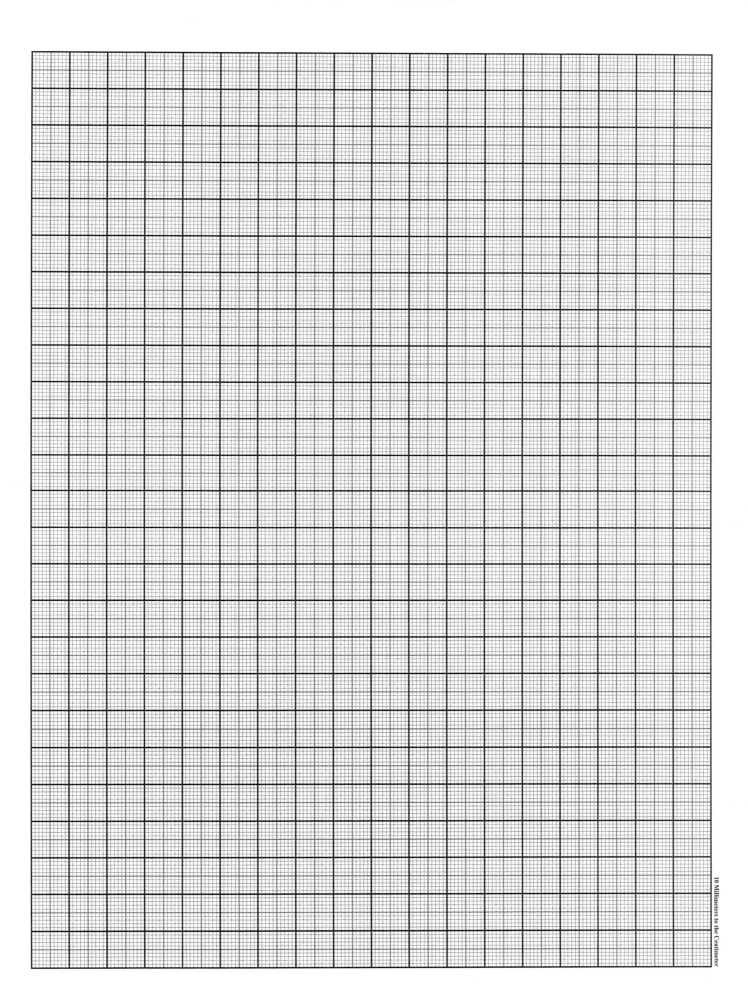

10 Millimeters to the Centimeter

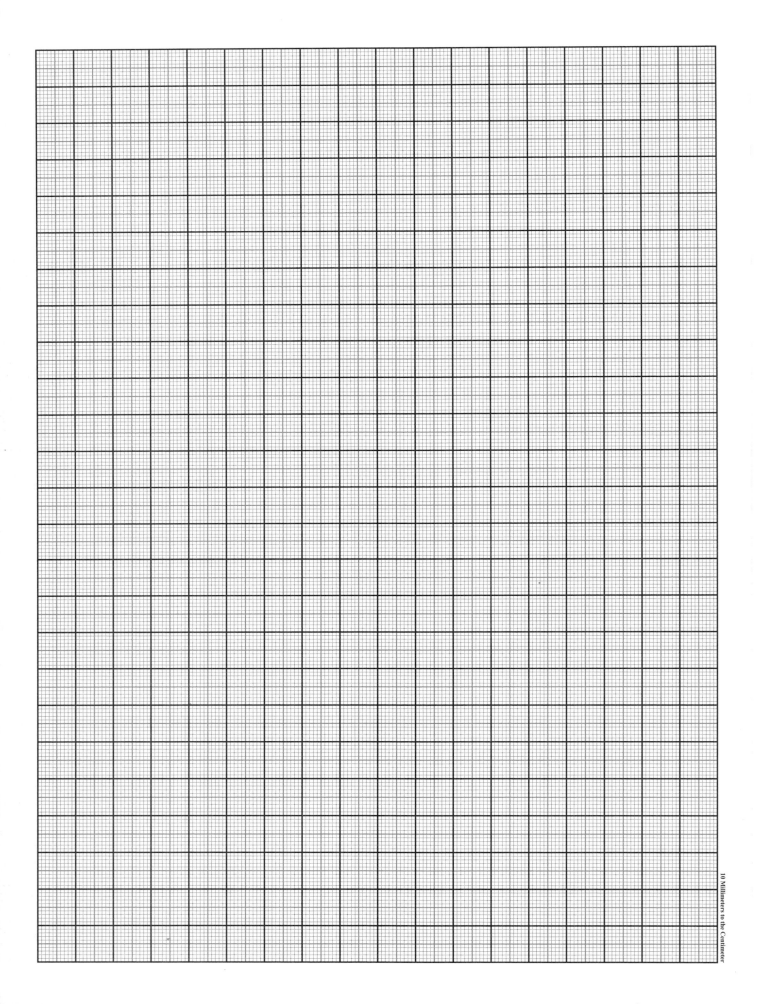

10 Millimeters to the Centimeter

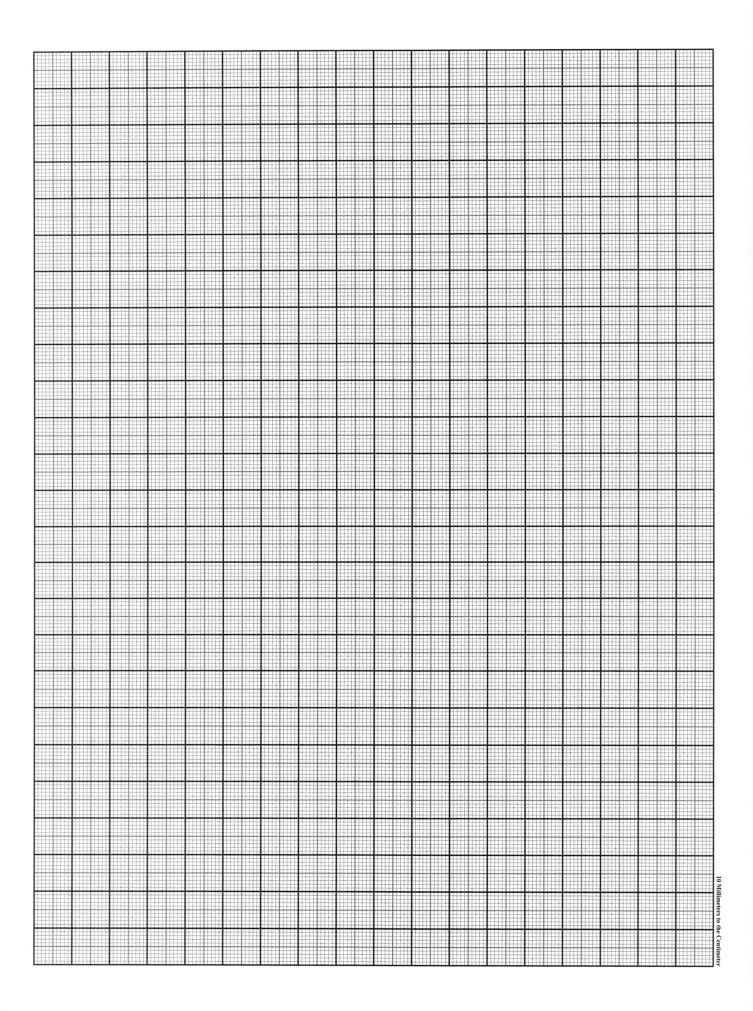

10 Millimeters to the Centimeter

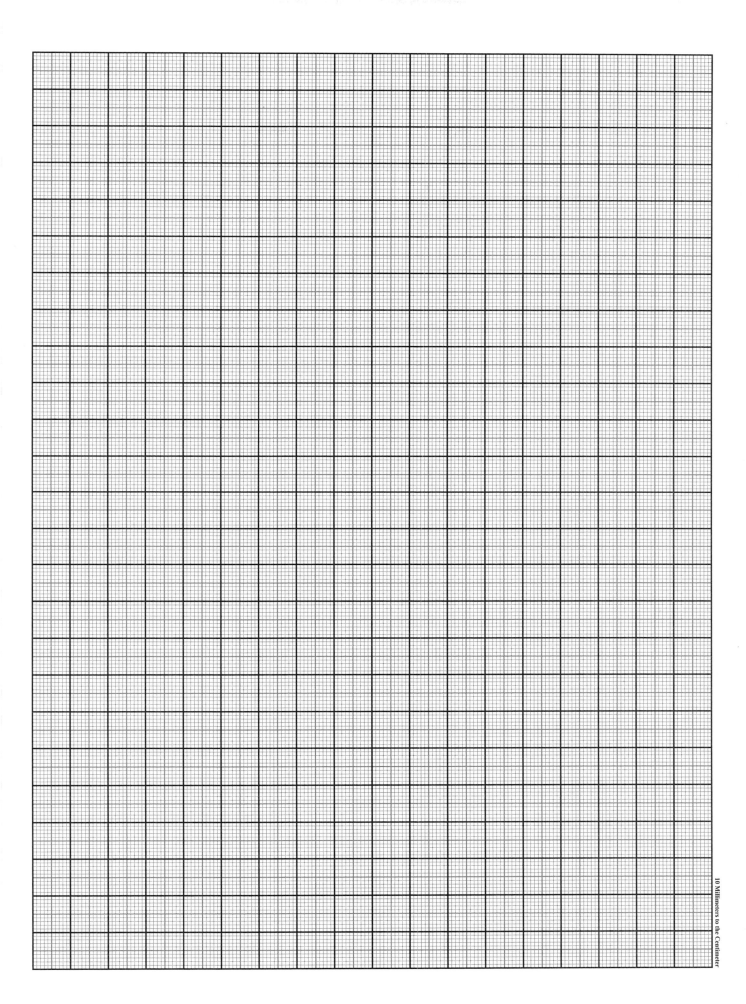

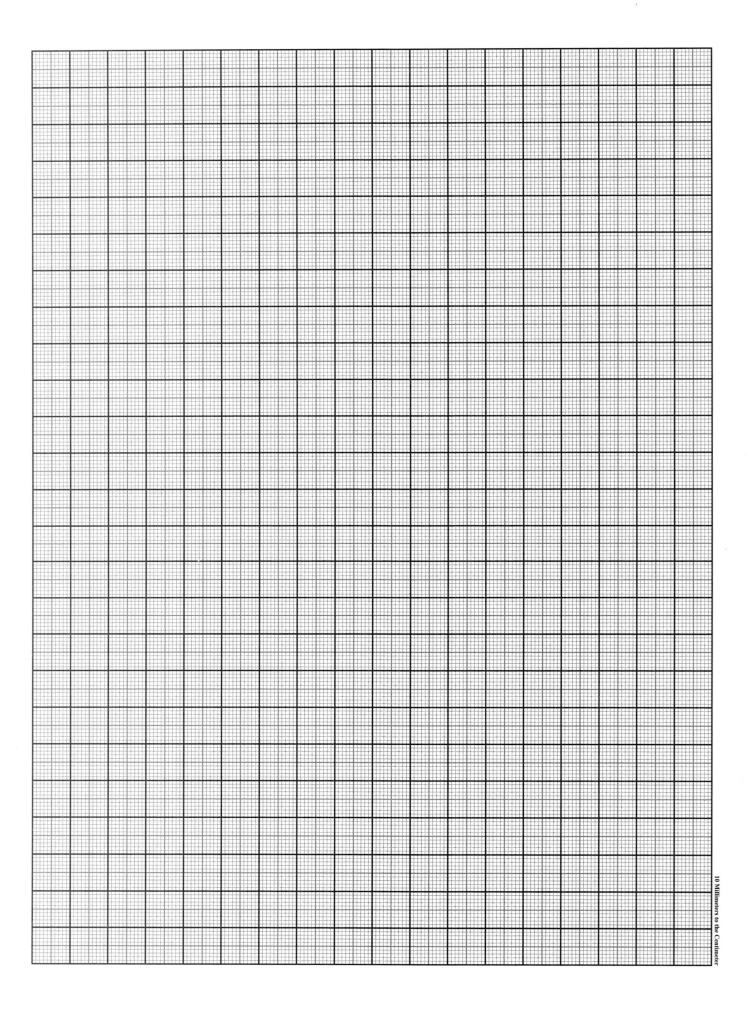

10 Millimeters to the Centimeter

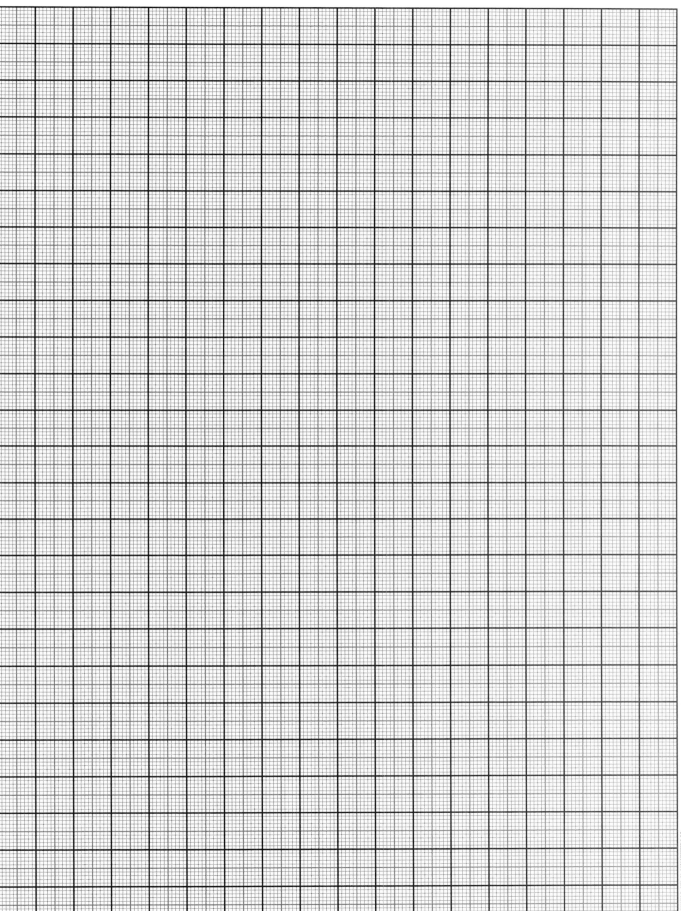

10 Millimeters to the Centimeter

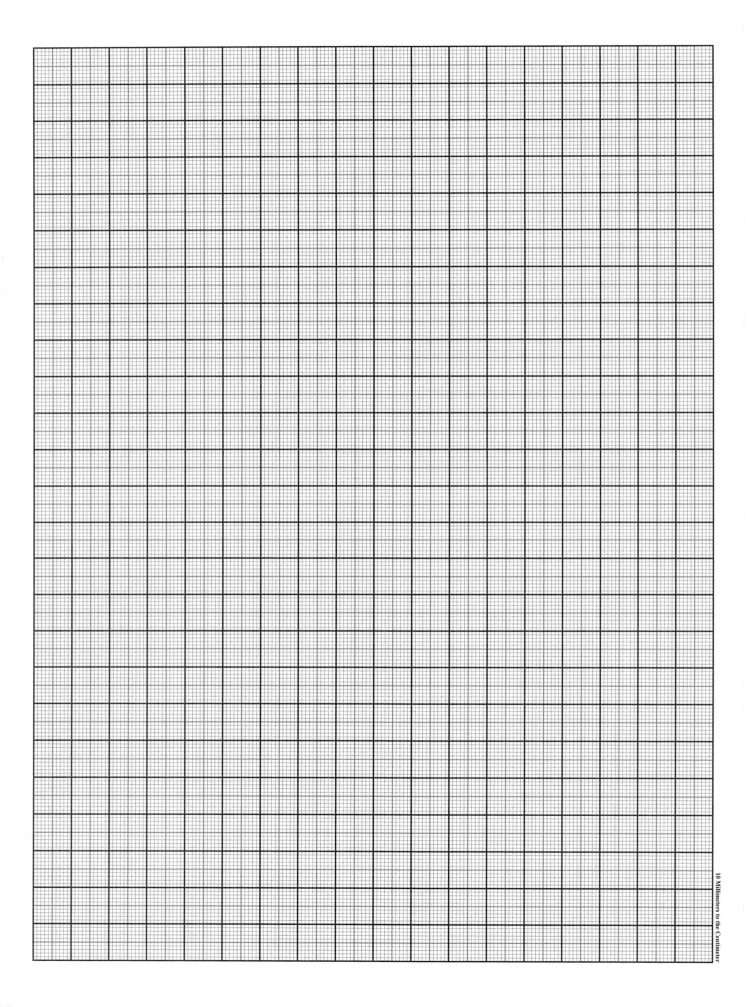

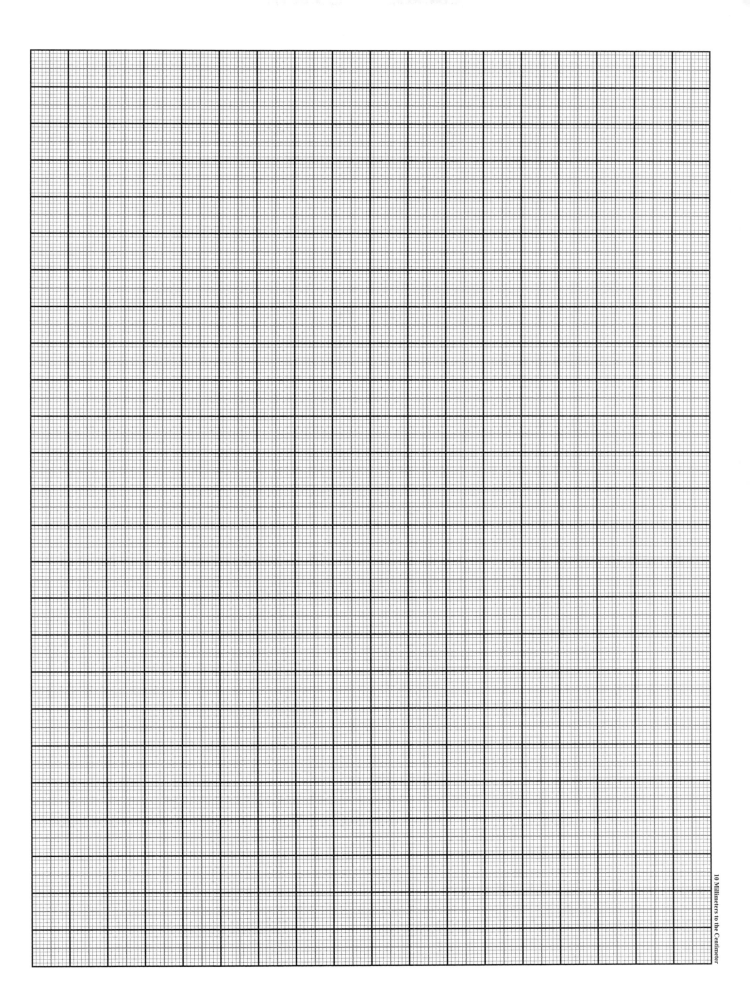

10 Millimeters to the Centimeter

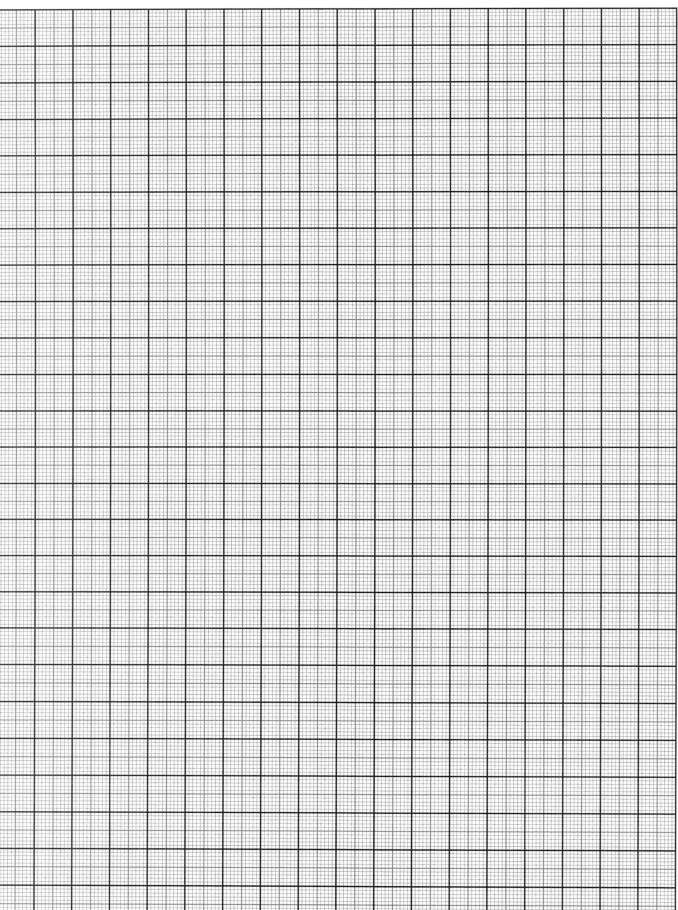

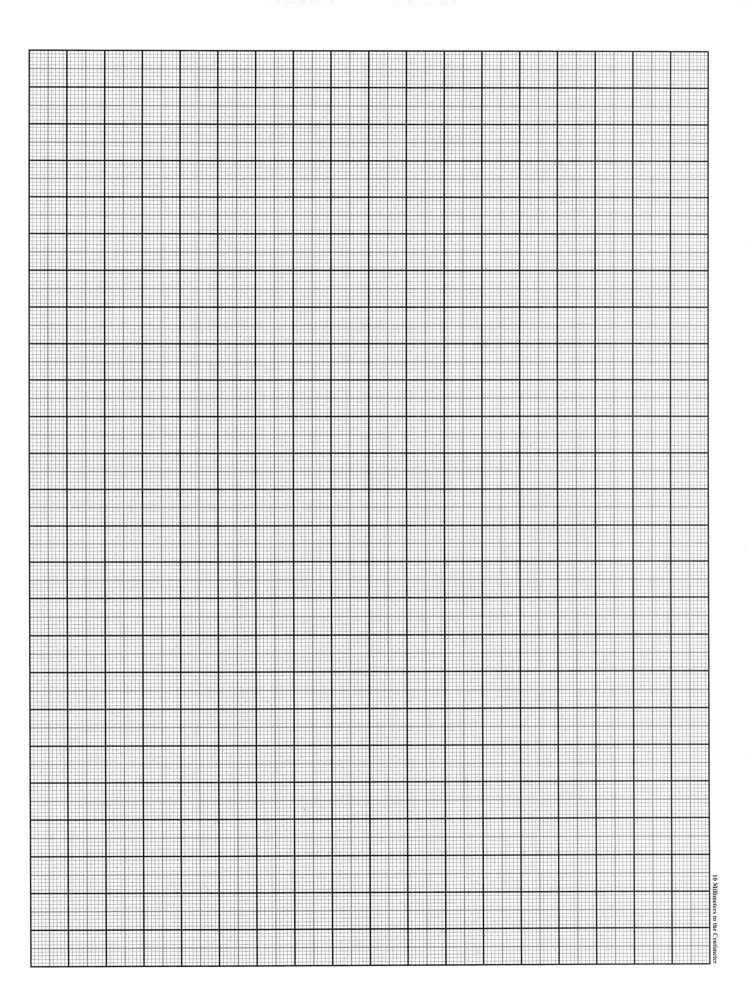

10 Millimeters to the Centimeter

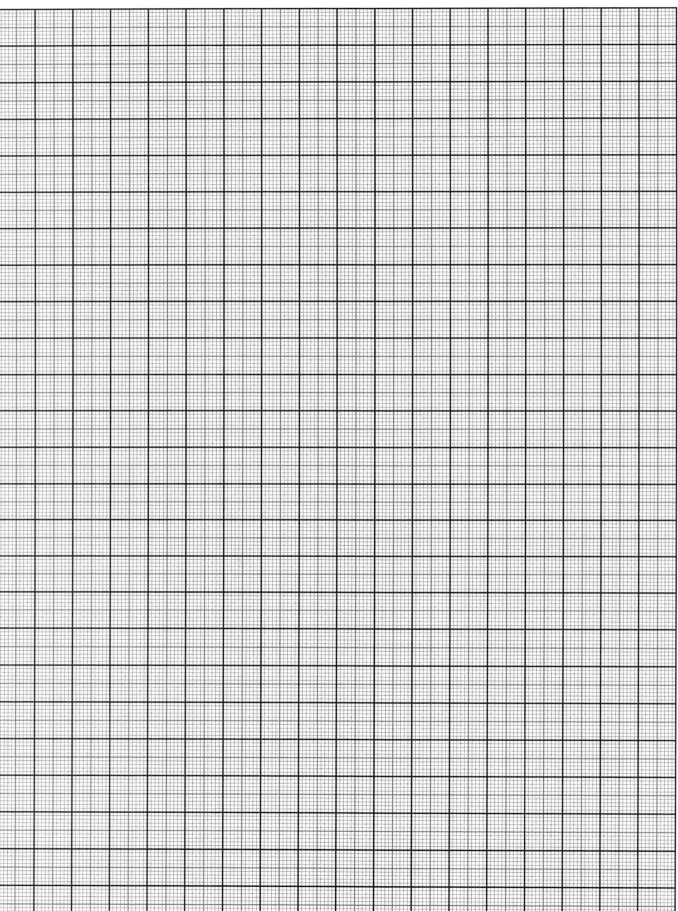

10 Millimeters to the Centimeter

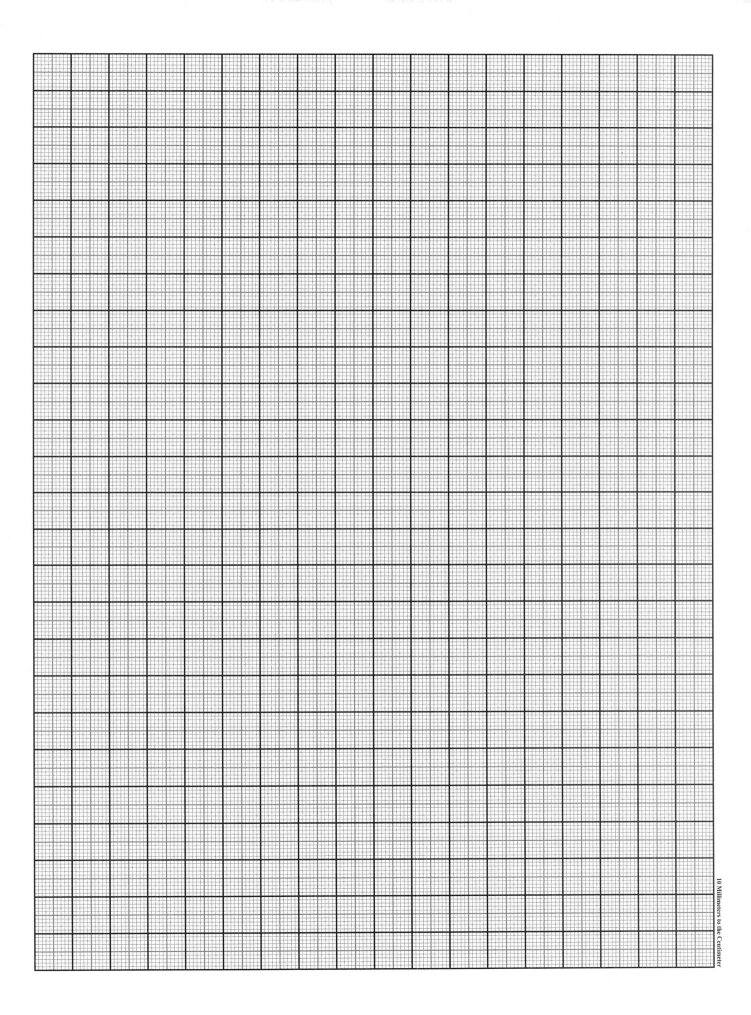

10 Millimeters to the Centimeter

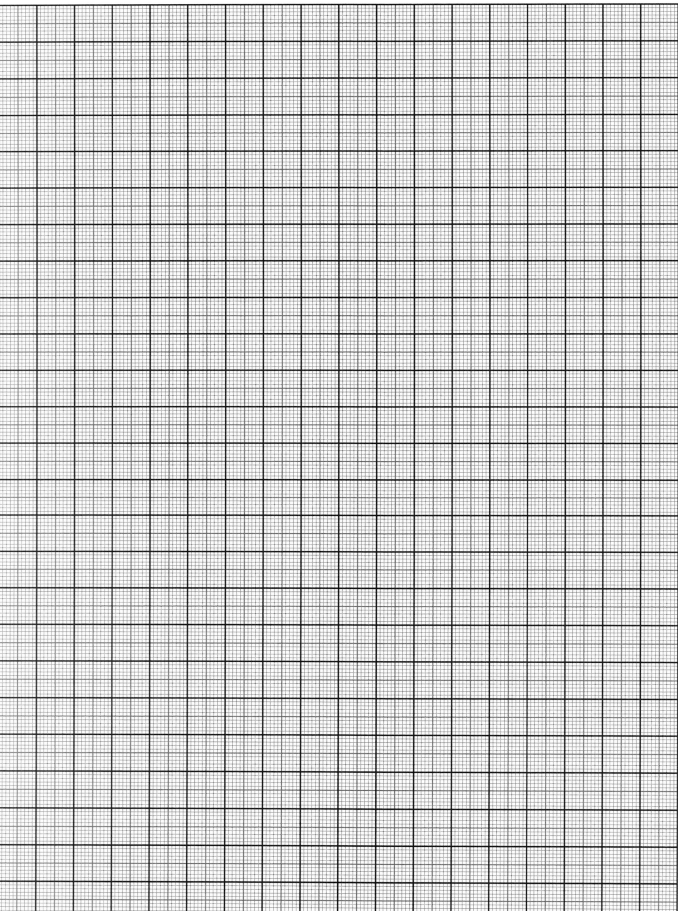

10 Millimeters to the Centimeter

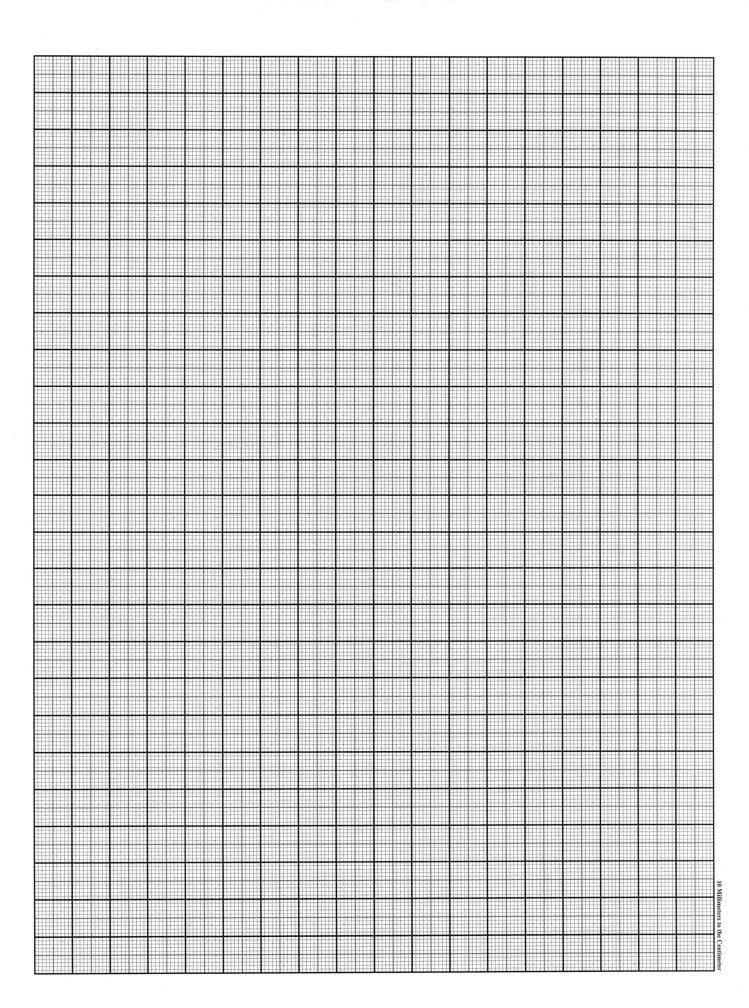

10 Millimeters to the Centimeter

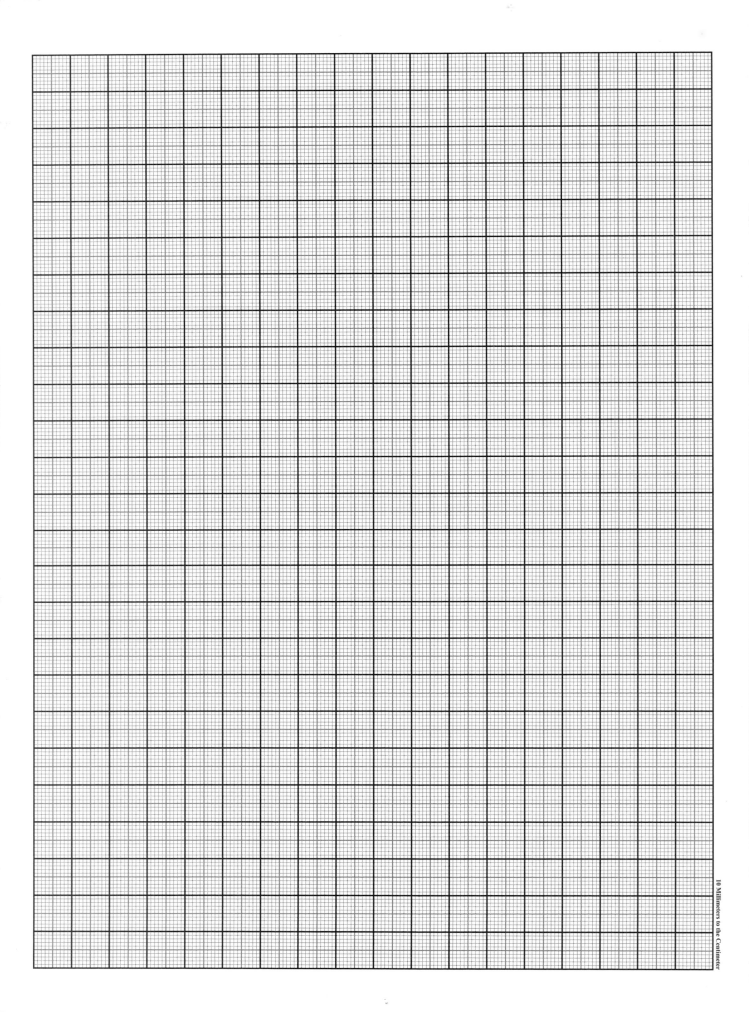

10 Millimeters to the Centimeter